Houghton Mifflin

California Math

Daily Routines
and Practice

Student Book

- Daily Routines
- Practice
- Looking Ahead
  Activities

GRADE

5

Visit **Education Place**®
www.eduplace.com/kids

 HOUGHTON MIFFLIN   BOSTON

Printed in the U.S.A.

ISBN 10: 0-618-96003-1
ISBN 13: 978-0-618-96003-3

5 6 7 8 9 1429 16 15 14 13 12 11 10 09

Hands On: Find Prime Numbers

Problem of the Day ———————————————— MR 1.1

In a three digit number, the ones digit is the greatest digit possible, the tens digit is 3 less than the ones digit, and the hundreds digit is half the tens digit. What is the number?

Number Sense ———————————————— Grade 4 KEY NS 1.3

Round the given number to the underlined digit.

1. 3<u>9</u>5

2. <u>3</u>480

3. <u>4</u>7,298

Number of the Day ———————————————— MR 1.1

27

What are some ways, using addition or multiplication, to make 27?

_____

_____

_____

Facts Practice ———————————————— KEY AF 1.2

Find the missing factor.

1. $9 \times$ ___ $= 54$
2. ___ $\times 5 = 35$
3. $7 \times$ ___ $= 56$

4. ___ $\times 6 = 24$
5. $6 \times$ ___ $= 36$
6. ___ $\times 8 = 80$

Hands On: Find Prime Numbers

CA Standard
KEY NS 1.4

Draw rectangles to help you decide if a number is *prime*. Write *prime* or *not prime*.

1. 5

_____

2. 4

_____

3. 21

_____

4. 11

_____

5. 18

_____

6. 15

_____

Decide if the number is prime or not prime. You can draw arrays or use the Sieve of Eratosthenes.

7. 23

_____

8. 27

_____

9. 37

_____

10. 8

_____

11. 29

_____

12. 41

_____

Test Practice

Circle the letter of the correct answer.

13. Which number is a prime number?

A 5   C 6

B 12   D 4

14. Which number is *not* a prime number?

A 13   C 11

B 19   D 14

Writing Math How could Anita arrange 11 tiles to identify the number as *prime* or *not prime*?

_____

_____

_____

Find Factors of a Number

Problem of the Day ——————————————————— MR 1.1

Tammy has several different dates she can choose for the school
dance. She wants to pick a prime number. Which date should she pick?
January 9, February 15, March 19, April 21?

Number Sense ——————————————————— KEY NS 1.4

Write the given numbers as a product of their prime factors.

1. 25

2. 47

3. 38

Number of the Day ——————————————————— MR 1.1

24

Throughout the day, find ways to use the number 24.

_____

_____

_____

Facts Practice ——————————————————— KEY AF 1.2

Find the missing number.

1. 81 ÷ ____ = 9   **2.** 42 ÷ 7 = ____   **3.** ____ ÷ 3 = 9

4. ____ ÷ 6 = 4   **5.** 60 ÷ ____ = 10   **6.** 102 ÷ ____ = 34

Find Factors of a Number

CA Standards
KEY NS 1.4, MR 2.4

Draw arrays to find the factors of each number. Then write if the number is prime or composite.

1. 9 _____

_____

2. 37 _____

_____

3. 21 _____

_____

_____

4. 32 _____

_____

5. 41 _____

_____

6. 36 _____

_____

_____

7. 33 _____

_____

8. 19 _____

_____

9. 11 _____

_____

Use division to find the factors of each number. Then write if the number is prime or composite.

10. 35 _____

_____

11. 51 _____

_____

12. 15 _____

_____

13. 12 _____

_____

14. 10 _____

_____

15. 50 _____

_____

 **Test Practice**

Circle the letter of the correct answer.

16. Which number is a composite number?

A 93   C 47

B 67   D 31

17. Drew was making a list of all of the factors of 24. Which list shows the correct factors for 24?

A 1, 24   C 1, 3, 8, 24

B 1, 3, 4, 6, 8, 24   D 1, 2, 3, 4, 6, 8, 12, 24

Writing Math Tyler has 52 red tiles. Describe the different arrays that Tyler can make using the tiles.

Name _____ Date _____

Prime Factorization

Problem of the Day ———————————————— KEY NS 1.4

The director of an art museum has between 45 and 55 paintings to display. He wishes to display an equal number on each of two walls. How many paintings could the museum display? Give as many answers as possible.

Number Sense ———————————————— KEY NS 1.4

Determine if the number is prime or composite.

1. 32

2. 47

3. 29

Word of the Day ———————————————— KEY NS 1.2

pattern

Create your own number pattern. For example: 2, 10, 18, 26, 34...

_____

_____

Facts Practice ———————————————— Grade 4 KEY NS 3.2

Divide mentally.

1. 720 ÷ 8   2. 4,900 ÷ 7   3. 810 ÷ 9

4. 4,000 ÷ 50   5. 2,400 ÷ 80   6. 630 ÷ 90

Prime Factorization

CA Standards
KEY NS 1.4, MR 2.3

Complete the factor tree. Then write the prime factorization.

1.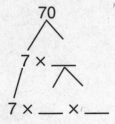

   70
   7 × ___
   7 × ___ × ___

   _____

2.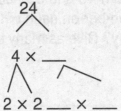

   24
   4 × ___
   2 × 2 ___ × ___

   _____

3.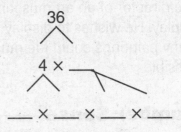

   36
   4 × ___
   ___ × ___ × ___ × ___

   _____

Write the prime factorization of each number. If the number is prime, write *prime*.

4. 20 _____

5. 21 _____

6. 22 _____

7. 23 _____

8. 24 _____

9. 25 _____

10. 26 _____

11. 27 _____

12. 28 _____

13. 29 _____

14. 30 _____

15. 31 _____

Test Practice

Circle the letter of the correct answer.

16. Write the prime factorization of 27.

    A 3 × 9   C 3 × 3 × 3

    B 2 × 3 × 9   D 9 × 3

17. What is the prime factorization of 54?

    A 2 × 3 × 3 × 3   C 2 × 3 × 3

    B 6 × 3 × 3   D 6 × 9

Writing Math Explain how you can make more than one factor tree to show the prime factorization for the number 16.

_____

_____

_____

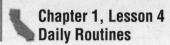
Exponents and Prime Factorization

Problem of the Day ———————————————— KEY

The Rockets scored 56 points in their basketball game. What is the prime factorization of 56?

Number Sense ——————————————————— KEY

Determine if the number is prime or composite.

1. 9

2. 17

3. 53

Word of the Day ——————————————————— NS 1.3

power

How is the word *power* used in every day language?

_____

_____

_____

Facts Practice ——————————————————— KEY

Write the prime factorization of the number.

1. 16   **2.** 20

3. 45   **4.** 54

Exponents and Prime Factorization

CA Standards
KEY NS 1.4, NS 1.3

Write each expression using exponents.

1. $2 \times 2 \times 2 \times 2 \times 2$ _____

2. $3 \times 3 \times 3 \times 3$ _____

3. $5 \times 5 \times 5$ _____

Write using a repeated factor. Find the value.

4. 6^2 _____

5. 7^1 _____

6. 4^3 _____

Write the prime factorization of each number. Use exponents if possible. If the number is prime, write prime.

7. 21 _____

8. 32 _____

9. 36 _____

10. 41 _____

11. 75 _____

12. 67 _____

 **Test Practice**

Circle the letter of the correct answer.

13. Write 24 using repeated factors.

   A 2×4

   B 4×4

   C $2 \times 2 \times 2 \times 3$

   D 2×2

14. What is the prime factorization of 44?

   A $4^2 \times 11$

   B $2^2 \times 11$

   C 4×11

   D $2 \times 2 \times 2 \times 11$

Writing Math How can exponents make it easier to write an expression with a repeated factor in the product?

_____

_____

_____

Name _____ Date _____

Common Factors and Greatest Common Factor

Problem of the Day ————————————————————— KEY NS 1.4

Each dimension of a cube is 4 inches. Express $4 \times 4 \times 4$ using exponents.

Number Sense ——————————————————————— KEY NS 1.4

Determine the base and the exponent of each.

1. 9^3

2. 2^5

3. 3^8

Word of the Day ———————————————————————— MR 2.3

common

Give some examples of things that you have in common with another classmate.

_____

_____

_____

Facts Practice ———————————————————————— MR 2.4

Multiply.

1. $5 \times 3 \times 4$ **2.** $6 \times 9 \times 4$

3. $4 \times 7 \times 3$ **4.** $9 \times 7 \times 5$

Name _____ Date _____

Common Factors and Greatest Common Factor

CA Standards
KEY NS 1.4, MR 2.4

List the factors of each number. Circle the common factors. Then find the greatest common factor of the numbers.

1. 28 _____

32 _____

_____

2. 12 _____

18 _____

_____

3. 20 _____

40 _____

_____

4. 16 _____

32 _____

_____

5. 35 _____

42 _____

_____

6. 20 _____

33 _____

_____

Write the prime factorization of each number. Then find the greatest common factor (GCF) of the numbers.

7. 12 _____

15 _____

_____

8. 8 _____

18 _____

_____

9. 10 _____

45 _____

_____

Test Practice

Circle the letter of the correct answer.

10. Tia made 50 cupcakes and 160 cookies for a bake sale. She put the items in packages with an equal number of cupcakes and cookies. How many packages did she make?

A 2   C 3

B 5   D 10

11. Monique had 18 pictures of friends and 42 pictures of family to place in her scrapbook. She wants to place the same number of pictures of family and friends on each page. How many pages can she complete?

A 2   C 3

B 6   D 18

 Writing Math Can two numbers have more than one greatest common factor (GCF)? Why or why not?

_____

_____

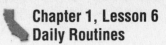
Problem Solving: Field Trip

Problem of the Day ———————————————————— MR 2.4

There are 24 students waiting to see the Escher exhibit and 16 students waiting to see the fractal exhibit. What are the largest equal-size groups the class could be divided into?

Number Sense ———————————————————————— KEY NS 1.4

Find the greatest common factor (GCF) of the numbers.

1. 24, 12

2. 10, 15

3. 48, 64

Number of the Day ————————————————————— MR 2.4

28

Write 28 as a product of factors in four different ways.

_____

_____

_____

Facts Practice ———————————————————————— KEY NS 1.4

Write the prime factorization of each number.

1. 40   2. 32   3. 45

4. 108   5. 450   6. 1,600

Hands On: Represent Fractions

Problem of the Day
KEY

I am thinking of two numbers between 20 and 30. Their greatest common factor is 7. What are the numbers?

Number Sense
KEY

Find the greatest common factor.

1. 6 and 9

2. 30 and 42

3. 18 and 54

Number of the Day
MR 2.3

2

List some sports that have 2 players on a team.

_____

_____

_____

Facts Practice
MR 2.6

Find the missing factor.

1. $9 \times ? = 72$

2. $? \times 5 = 45$

3. $6 \times ? = 24$

4. $? \times 11 = 77$

5. $? \times 8 = 96$

Hands On: Represent Fractions

CA Standards
KEY NS 1.5, MR 2.3

Draw a shaded model for each fraction.

1. $\frac{3}{8}$ **2.** $\frac{4}{5}$ **3.** $\frac{13}{15}$

Draw a number line and show the position of each fraction.

4. $\frac{1}{3}$ **5.** $\frac{4}{3}$ **6.** $\frac{10}{5}$

Draw a model to show each fraction as a division expression. Write the division expression.

7. $\frac{4}{2}$ _____   **8.** $\frac{7}{3}$ _____

Test Practice

Circle the letter of the correct answer.

9. Which letter on the number line could represent $\frac{5}{12}$?

A A   C C

B B   D D

10. Identify the fraction shown in the model.

A $\frac{1}{7}$ C $\frac{1}{8}$

B $\frac{7}{8}$ D $\frac{8}{7}$

Writing Math Explain how division can be used to represent fractions.

_____

_____

Fractions and Mixed Numbers

Problem of the Day ———————————————————— MR 2.3

Derek's basketball team has 8 players. Two players are sick. Model a fraction that represents the number of players that will be able to play the next game.

Number Sense ———————————————————— KEY NS 2.3

Write each fraction.

1. five-eighths

2. seven-tenths

3. one-fourth

4. two-twelfths

5. ten-thirteenths

Word of the Day ———————————————————— MR 2.3

mixed

Name some items that are mixed.

_____

_____

Facts Practice ———————————————————— MR 2.6

Solve.

1. $(5 \times 3) + 2$ 2. $(9 \times 4) + 5$ 3. $(3 \times 4) + 1$

4. $(6 \times 8) + 4$ 5. $(4 \times 7) + 3$

Fractions and Mixed Numbers

Study this number line. Write each missing fraction. Then draw a picture to represent each missing fraction.

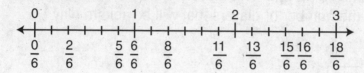

1. _____

Write each improper fraction as a mixed number or a whole number.

2. $\frac{11}{6}$ _____

3. $\frac{13}{5}$ _____

4. $\frac{7}{4}$ _____

5. $\frac{12}{6}$ _____

6. $\frac{15}{2}$ _____

Write each mixed number as an improper fraction.

7. $2\frac{1}{3}$ _____

8. $3\frac{4}{5}$ _____

9. $4\frac{2}{5}$ _____

10. $5\frac{1}{6}$ _____

11. $2\frac{4}{5}$ _____

 Test Practice

Circle the letter of the correct answer.

12. Tony needs to frame 7 pictures. He has framed 4 so far. What fraction represents the pictures he has not framed?

   A $\frac{3}{7}$ C $\frac{4}{7}$

   B $\frac{2}{7}$ D $\frac{7}{7}$

13. Which point on the number line best represents $4\frac{2}{3}$?

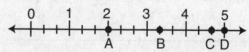

   A Point A   C Point C

   B Point B   D Point D

Writing Math What operations are used to change a mixed number to an improper fraction? Explain.

_____

_____

_____

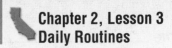
Equivalent Fractions and Simplest Form

Problem of the Day KEY NS 1.4

Miguel ordered $\frac{10}{8}$ pounds of ham for a meat tray. What is $\frac{10}{8}$ as a mixed number?

Number Sense KEY NS 1.5

Write each improper fraction as a mixed number or mixed number as an improper fraction.

1. $\frac{3}{2}$

2. $4\frac{2}{3}$

3. $\frac{12}{3}$

Word of the Day KEY NS 1.2

equivalent

What does equivalent mean? Discuss things or objects that are equivalent.

_____

_____

_____

Facts Practice ————————————————— KEY NS 1.4

Find the Greatest Common Factor of each number pair.

1. 15, 6   2. 4, 16   3. 10, 45

4. 18, 21   5. 24, 30   6. 12, 24

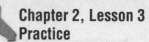

Name _____ Date _____

Equivalent Fractions and Simplest Form

CA Standards
KEY NS 2.3, **KEY** NS 1.5

Complete.

1. $\frac{16}{20} = \frac{}{5}$

2. $\frac{3}{4} = \frac{15}{}$

3. $\frac{42}{48} = \frac{}{8}$

4. $\frac{2}{6} = \frac{}{18}$

5. $\frac{49}{21} = \frac{}{3}$

6. $\frac{12}{18} = \frac{2}{}$

7. $\frac{5}{9} = \frac{}{72}$

8. $1\frac{8}{12} = \frac{}{3}$

Simplify each fraction.

9. $\frac{12}{30}$ _____

10. $\frac{33}{18}$ _____

11. $\frac{28}{8}$ _____

12. $\frac{25}{40}$ _____

13. $\frac{24}{38}$ _____

14. $\frac{28}{12}$ _____

15. $\frac{36}{30}$ _____

16. $\frac{18}{27}$ _____

17. $\frac{24}{44}$ _____

18. $\frac{35}{15}$ _____

19. $\frac{14}{42}$ _____

20. $\frac{48}{12}$ _____

21. $\frac{22}{8}$ _____

22. $\frac{26}{32}$ _____

23. $\frac{36}{24}$ _____

24. $\frac{18}{39}$ _____

Test Practice

Circle the letter of the correct answer.

25. Which shows $\frac{40}{64}$ in simplest form?

   A $\frac{10}{18}$ C $\frac{5}{9}$

   B $\frac{5}{8}$ D $\frac{2}{3}$

26. Marcos spelled 98 of the 100 spelling words correctly. Which pair of fractions are both equivalent to his score?

   A $\frac{98}{100}, \frac{48}{50}$ C $\frac{49}{50}, \frac{196}{200}$

   B $\frac{49}{50}, \frac{99}{100}$ D $\frac{99}{100}, \frac{198}{200}$

Writing Math How do you know when a fraction is written in simplest form?

_____

_____

Name _____ Date _____

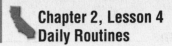

Compare Fractions

Problem of the Day ———————————————— KEY NS 2.3

Two-thirds of the bagels in an order are plain. There are 48 bagels in the order. How many bagels are plain?

Number Sense ———————————————————— KEY NS 1.5

Write a fraction equivalent to the given fraction.

1. $\frac{20}{35}$

2. $\frac{24}{36}$

3. $\frac{16}{40}$

Number of the Day ———————————————— KEY NS 1.2

$\frac{1}{2}$

Throughout the day, find ways that you use the fraction $\frac{1}{2}$.

_____

_____

_____

Facts Practice ———————————————————— KEY NS 1.4

Write each fraction in simplest form.

1. $\frac{6}{15}$ 2. $\frac{4}{16}$ 3. $\frac{8}{10}$

4. $\frac{9}{18}$ 5. $\frac{24}{30}$ 6. $\frac{12}{24}$

Name _____ Date _____

Compare Fractions

CA Standards
KEY NS 1.5, MR 1.1

Compare these fractions. Use a number line to help. Write <, >, or = for each ◯.

1. $\frac{5}{6}$ ◯ $\frac{3}{5}$ 2. $\frac{3}{8}$ ◯ $\frac{4}{7}$ 3. $\frac{9}{11}$ ◯ $\frac{5}{7}$ 4. $\frac{4}{12}$ ◯ $\frac{6}{18}$ 5. $\frac{3}{8}$ ◯ $\frac{4}{5}$

Compare these fractions. Find a common denominator. Write <, >, = for each ◯.

6. $\frac{3}{5}$ ◯ $\frac{1}{2}$ 7. $\frac{7}{8}$ ◯ $\frac{5}{6}$ 8. $\frac{2}{9}$ ◯ $\frac{1}{4}$ 9. $\frac{3}{7}$ ◯ $\frac{2}{5}$ 10. $\frac{5}{10}$ ◯ $\frac{4}{6}$

11. $\frac{2}{5}$ ◯ $\frac{3}{8}$ 12. $\frac{8}{14}$ ◯ $\frac{4}{7}$ 13. $\frac{5}{6}$ ◯ $\frac{3}{4}$ 14. $\frac{4}{9}$ ◯ $\frac{5}{8}$ 15. $\frac{3}{7}$ ◯ $\frac{4}{8}$

 **Test Practice**

Circle the letter of the correct answer.

16. Which letter on the number line best identifies a location greater than $\frac{3}{5}$?

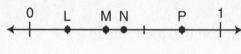

A L   C M

B N   D P

17. Compare $\frac{6}{15}$ and $\frac{2}{3}$.

A $\frac{6}{15} < \frac{2}{3}$ C $\frac{6}{15} > \frac{2}{3}$

B $\frac{6}{15} = \frac{2}{3}$ D $\frac{2}{3} < \frac{6}{15}$

Writing Math Explain why finding a common denominator
makes it easier to compare fractions.

_____

_____

_____

Name _____ Date _____

Problem Solving: Compare Data Sets

Problem of the Day ─────────────────────── MR 1.1

The students in the school voted for red or blue to be used as the school color. Two thirds of the students in the school voted for red. Three fifths voted for blue. Which color did fewer people choose?

Number Sense ─────────────────────── KEY NS 1.5

Compare the fractions. Write <, >, or = for the .

1. $\frac{2}{3}$ ⬭ $\frac{11}{12}$

2. $\frac{3}{5}$ ⬭ $\frac{1}{2}$

3. $\frac{3}{8}$ ⬭ $\frac{6}{16}$

Number of the Day ─────────────────────── KEY NS 1.5

$\frac{3}{4}$

Between which two whole numbers will $\frac{3}{4}$ be located on a number line?
Represent $\frac{3}{4}$ on a number line.

_____

_____

_____

Facts Practice ─────────────────────── KEY NS 1.5

Write each fraction in simplest form.

1. $\frac{20}{35}$ 2. $\frac{25}{36}$ 3. $\frac{40}{100}$

4. $\frac{16}{40}$ 5. $\frac{12}{48}$ 6. $\frac{24}{36}$

Problem Solving: Compare Data Sets

CA Standard
KEY MR 1.1, SDAP 1.3

Solve. Explain why your answer makes sense.

1. A monkey climbed up 15 feet of a 25 foot tree. A snake slithered up 9 feet of a 12 foot tree. Which animal traveled the greatest fraction of a tree?

_____

2. A 6-year-old hippo has been in a zoo for 3 years. A 10-year-old giraffe has been in the same zoo for 6 years. Which animal has been in the zoo for a greater fraction of time?

_____

3. The female penguins ate 16 pounds of fish out of 20 pounds of food. The male penguins ate 20 out of 25 pounds. Did the female or male penguins eat a greater fraction of fish?

_____

4. A turtle spent 45 out of 60 minutes sitting on the rock. An alligator spent 20 out of 30 minutes on the rock. Which animal spent the greater fraction of time on the rock?

_____

Test Practice

Circle the letter of the correct answer.

5. The sea lions ate 18 out of 24 pounds of fish and the seals ate 25 out of 35 pounds of fish. Which shows the greatest fraction of fish eaten in simplest form?

A $\frac{18}{24}$ C $\frac{25}{35}$

B $\frac{3}{4}$ D $\frac{5}{7}$

6. In the past 24 hours an alligator spent 12 hours in the water and 10 hours on land. Which shows the greatest amount of time spent by the alligator in simplest form?

A $\frac{12}{24}$ C $\frac{10}{24}$

B $\frac{1}{2}$ D $\frac{5}{12}$

Writing Math Explain how making a table can help you compare data sets.

_____

_____

Name _____ Date _____

Hands On: Represent Whole Numbers and Decimals

Problem of the Day
KEY **NS 1.5**

Each student in the class voted on their favorite color. Two fifths of the students voted for red. One fourth voted for green. Did more students choose red or green?

Number Sense
KEY **NS 1.5**

Use Workmat 3 to represent the fractions $\frac{2}{3}$ and $\frac{7}{12}$ on a number line. Then, compare the fractions and circle the greater fraction.

Number of the Day
KEY **NS 1.5**

5

If a number line is divided into thirds, what improper fraction would represent 5?

_____

_____

_____

Facts Practice
MR 1.1

Find the missing number.

1. $\frac{3}{5} = \frac{\blacksquare}{20}$

2. $\frac{5}{6} = \frac{25}{\blacksquare}$

3. $\frac{\blacksquare}{8} = \frac{15}{40}$

4. $\frac{7}{\blacksquare} = \frac{21}{36}$

5. $\frac{11}{6} = 1\frac{\blacksquare}{6}$

6. $\frac{15}{6} = 2\frac{1}{\blacksquare}$

Hands On: Represent Whole Numbers and Decimals

CA Standard
NS 1.1

Write the decimal notation for the word form of the number.

1. five and four tenths

_____

2. three and twenty-five hundredths

_____

3. seventy-two thousandths

_____

4. twelve and fifteen hundredths

_____

5. twenty and thirty-three thousandths

_____

6. twenty-five and eight hundredths

_____

Write the money amount using decimal notation from the bills and coins below.

7.

_____

8.

_____

9.

_____

Test Practice

Circle the letter of the correct answer.

10. Write the money amount in decimal notation for five dollars and thirty-five cents.

   A $5.35   C $5.30

   B $5.55   D $5.33

11. Which number does NOT represent 1.42?

   A one and forty-two hundredths

   B $1.42

   C $1\frac{42}{100}$

   D one hundred forty-two thousandths

Writing Math Jack modeled the decimal 13.21 using the following bills and coins: 1 $10 bill, 3 $1 bills, 4 nickels and a penny. Did Jack use the fewest bills and coins? Explain.

_____

_____

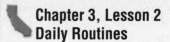
Place Value Through Billions

Problem of the Day ———————————————————— NS 1.1

Diego saw a sign that one gallon of gasoline costs $2.008. Does this amount represent two dollars and eight cents? Explain your answer.

Number Sense ————————————————————————— NS 1.1

Write the fraction notation for each decimal.

1. 8.7

2. 8.27

3. 8.327

Number of the Day ———————————————————— NS 1.1

8

Eight is greater than 7.921. What is an example of a decimal through thousandths that is greater than 8?

_____

_____

_____

Facts Practice ————————————————————————— NS 1.1

Round the amount to the nearest hundredth of a dollar.

1. $5.789

2. $7.597

3. $59.023

4. $176.435

5. $849.986

6. $1,277.158

Name _____ Date _____

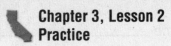
Place Value Through Billions

Write each number in standard form and in word form.

1. 6 thousand, 430

2. 549 thousand, 318

_____

_____

_____

3. 80,000 + 20 + 7

4. 200,000 + 10,000 + 9,000 + 53

_____

_____

_____

_____

Write each number in expanded form using exponents.

5. 74,285

6. 212,947

_____

_____

_____

_____

Test Practice

Circle the letter of the correct answer.

7. The boundary line between the United States and Canada is 3,987 miles. What is the value of the digit 9?

  A 9000   **C** 900

  B 90   **D** 9

8. What is the standard form of three hundred sixty thousand, fifty three?

  A 3,060,530   **C** 360,053

  B 306,053   **D** 36,053

Writing Math Explain how the number 23,565 can be represented by powers of 10.

_____

_____

_____

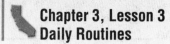
Place Value Through Thousandths

Problem of the Day ————————————————————————— NS 1.0

Use the digits 0–9 to write a ten-digit whole number. Use each digit only
once. What are the least and greatest possible numbers if the digit 3 is in
the billions place and the digit 9 is in the millions place?

Number Sense ————————————————————————————— NS 1.3

Write the number in standard form.

1. $(3 \times 10^3) + (9 \times 10^1)$

2. $(5 \times 10^2) + (4 \times 10^0)$

3. $(6 \times 10^4) + (8 \times 10^2)$

Word of the Day ———————————————————————————— NS 1.0

standard form

Give an example of numbers in standard form that you see throughout
the day.

_____

_____

_____

Facts Practice ————————————————————————————— NS 1.0

Write the value of the underlined digit.

1. 3,<u>5</u>89

2. 8<u>9</u>,209,627

3. 4,<u>2</u>43,578,106

4. 7,3<u>8</u>6,918

5. 54,32<u>6</u>

Name _____ Date _____

Place Value Through Thousandths

CA Standard
NS 1.0

Write each decimal in standard form.

1. two hundredths _____

2. seventy-five thousandths _____

3. four hundred sixteen thousandths _____

4. twenty and three tenths _____

5. one and thirty-two hundredths _____

6. five hundred three thousandths _____

Write each decimal in word form.

7. 0.52

_____

_____

8. 0.023

_____

_____

9. 0.408

_____

_____

10. 10.3

_____

_____

11. 2.014

_____

_____

12. 8.21

_____

_____

 **Test Practice**

Circle the letter of the correct answer.

13. Which underlined digit has a value of four hundredths?

A 20.4̲53   C 4̲36.72

B 2.3̲48   D 1.004̲

14. Oak trees grow 0.055 inches a day. Which is the value in word form?

A fifty-five thousandths

B fifty-five thousands

C fifty-five hundreds

D fifty-five hundredths

Writing Math How does the word "and" help you read the number two and sixty-four thousandths?

_____

_____

_____

Use with text pp. 60–61

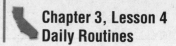

Compare and Order Whole Numbers and Decimals

Problem of the Day ———————————————————————— NS 1.0

Maria bought a piece of fabric that was forty-five hundredths of a yard long. The receipt said Maria bought 0.045 yards of fabric. Is the standard form of the decimal correct on the receipt? If not, give the correct standard form.

Number Sense ———————————————————————————————— NS 1.0

Write the place value of the underlined digit.

1. 77.5<u>2</u>

2. 0.89<u>3</u>

3. 16.1<u>4</u>6

Number of the Day ——————————————————————————— NS 1.0

0.6

Write as many sentences as you can using the number 0.6 accurately.

_____

_____

_____

Facts Practice ——————————————————————————————— NS 1.0

Write the value of the digit 5 in each number.

1. 67,592

2. 7.035

3. 5,243

4. 5.903

5. 3.256

6. 6.508

Name _____ Date _____

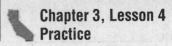

Compare and Order Whole Numbers and Decimals

CA Standards
NS 1.0, MR 2.0

Compare. Write >, <, or = for each ◯.

1. 3,471 ◯ 3,452　　**2.** 40,283 ◯ 40,567　　**3.** 1,042,639 ◯ 1,042,639

4. 0.0725 ◯ 0.725　　**5.** 12.462 ◯ 12.452

Order each set of numbers from greatest to least.

6. 2,437; 2,461; 2,459　　　　　　　**7.** 7.15, 7.51, 7.18

_____　　　　_____

Order each set of numbers from least to greatest.

8. 16.543, 16.453, 16.354　　　　　**9.** 2.589, 2.850, 2.590

_____　　　　_____

Test Practice

Circle the letter of the correct answer.

10. Which comparison is false?

  A 522 < 542

  B 203,541 > 201,982

  C 561,203,758 > 61,185

  D 462,075,114 < 460,789,532

11. Which shows the numbers in order from greatest to least?

  A 4.101, 4.011, 4.01

  B 4.011, 4.101, 4.01

  C 4.01, 4.011, 4.101

  D 4.101, 4.01, 4.011

Writing Math Explain how you would compare the whole numbers 38,458 and 38,560.

_____

_____

_____

_____

_____

Round Whole Numbers and Decimals

Problem of the Day ——————————————————————— NS 1.0

Joe needed 4.56 yards of fabric for a school project. He bought 4.76 yards of fabric. Did Joe buy enough fabric, too much fabric, or too little fabric?

Number Sense ——————————————————————————————— NS 1.0

Order the sets of numbers from greatest to least.

1. 2.68; 2.58; 3.78

2. 8; 7.59; 7.98

3. 1,459; 1,599; 1,489

Number of the Day ———————————————————————————— NS 1.0

1,459,889,263

What is a number that is greater than 1,459,889,263? What is a number that is less than 1,459,889,263?

_____

_____

_____

Facts Practice ——————————————————————————————— MR 2.0

Compare. Write >, <, or = in the ⬭.

1. 258,743 ⬭ 258, 723   **2.** 5.46 ⬭ 5.8   **3.** 38,508 ⬭ 35,946

4. 16.1 ⬭ 6.9   **5.** 1,258 ⬭ 1,463

Name _____ Date _____

Round Whole Numbers and Decimals

CA Standards
NS 1.1, MR 1.0

Round to the place indicated by the underlined digit.

1. <u>3</u>.099 _____

2. 0.2<u>6</u>8 _____

3. <u>6</u>.253 _____

4. <u>9</u>.972 _____

5. 27,<u>4</u>68 _____

6. 1<u>2</u>8,570 _____

7. 149,6<u>0</u>5 _____

8. <u>2</u>75,830 _____

Round each number.

9. 6.027 to the nearest hundredth _____

10. 208,478 to the nearest hundred _____

11. 5.071 to the nearest tenth _____

12. 452,099 to the nearest ten thousand _____

**Compare. Write >, <, or = for each ◯, given $a = 0.556$,
$b = 0.56$, $c = 0.056$, $d = 0.1$**

13. a ◯ b

14. c ◯ d

15. b ◯ c

16. d ◯ a

_____   _____   _____   _____

Find the digit that will make the inequality true.

17. $0.45 > 0.\square 9$

18. $0.\square 93 < 0.636$

19. $4.238 > 4.23\square$

_____   _____   _____

Test Practice

Circle the letter of the correct answer.

20. Which decimal is greater than 17.483?

   A 17.099

   C 17.384

   B 17.438

   D 17.504

21. What is 346.98 rounded to the nearest whole number?

   A 346

   C 446

   B 356

   D 347

Writing Math Explain how rounding whole numbers and decimals are similar.

_____

_____

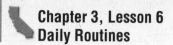
Problem Solving: Estimate or Exact?

Problem of the Day ——————————————————— NS 1.1

Gayle bought a piece of fabric that is 3.51 yards long. She rounded this amount to 4 yards. Does Gayle have about 4 yards of fabric? Explain your reasoning.

Number Sense ——————————————————————— NS 1.1

Round to the place indicated by the underlined digit.

1. 0.1̲94

2. 1.95̲6

3. 23̲3,578

Number of the Day ——————————————————— NS 1.1

4,000

Create a number that, when rounded to the nearest hundred, rounds to 4,000.

_____

_____

_____

Facts Practice ——————————————————————— NS 1.0

Write the value of the underlined digit.

1. 69̲3,218

2. 6.54̲3

3. 3,7̲02

4. 2.3̲18

5. 1̲,903,412

6. 61̲7,953,401,211

Problem Solving: Estimate or Exact? CA Standards MR 2.5, NS 1.1

Solve. Explain why you used an estimate or an exact answer.

Use the table to answer questions 1–2.

California Population Growth	
Year	**Population**
1950	10,586,223
1960	15,717,204
1970	19,971,069
1980	23,667,764
1990	29,760,021
2000	33,871,648

1. How many more people lived in California in 2000 than in 1950?

_____

_____

_____

2. Between which two decades did the population increase the most?

_____

_____

_____

Test Practice

Circle the letter of the correct answer.

3. Trevor needs $128,000 to pay for college. He already has saved $53,291. How much more money does he need?

   A $135,291   C $75,291

   B $74,709   D $75,000

4. Becky worked as a veterinarian's assistant for four years. She made $18,934 in her first year and $19,258 in her second year. Her third year she made $22,125, and in her fourth year she made $24,521. About how much money did Becky make over all four years?

   A $85,000   C $84,838

   B $84,000   D $83,728

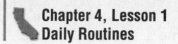
Hands On: Fractions and Decimals

Problem of the Day ———————————————————— NS 1.1

A five-digit number contains the digits 3, 4, 5, 6, and 7 in some order.
The number rounded to the nearest ten thousand is 40,000. The number
rounded to the nearest thousand is 37,000. The ones digit is one more
than the thousands digit. What is the number?

Number Sense Review ———————————————————— NS 1.1

Round to the place indicated by the underlined digit.

1. 935,005

2. 0.762

3. 96,012

Word of the Day ———————————————————— NS 1.1

round

During the day, find examples of when you round money amounts.

_____

_____

Facts Practice ———————————————————— NS 1.1

Write the fraction form for each decimal.

1. 2.4   2. 3.83   3. 21.569

4. 369.7   5. 140.635

Hands On: Fractions and Decimals

CA Standards
KEY NS 1.5, MR 2.3

Use the number line. Write each fraction as a decimal.

1. $\frac{1}{4}$

_____

2. $\frac{1}{10}$

_____

3. $\frac{2}{8}$

_____

4. $\frac{4}{5}$

_____

Test Practice

Circle the letter of the correct answer.

5. What is the decimal equivalent of $\frac{2}{8}$?

   A 0.5

   B 0.75

   C 0.25

   D 0.4

6. What is the fraction equivalent of 0.5?

   A $\frac{1}{2}$

   B $\frac{3}{4}$

   C $\frac{1}{3}$

   D $\frac{2}{8}$

Writing Math Explain how you can use number lines to compare fractions and decimals.

_____

_____

_____

_____

_____

_____

Equivalent Fractions and Decimals

Problem of the Day ———————————————— KEY NS 1.5

Diane needed to buy $\frac{3}{5}$ yard of ribbon for a project. She found one package with 0.35 yards of ribbon and another package with 0.6 yards. Which package of ribbon should Diane buy?

Number Sense Review ———————————————— KEY NS 1.5

Write each fraction as a decimal.

1. $\frac{9}{10}$

2. $\frac{2}{5}$

3. $\frac{1}{2}$

Number of the Day ———————————————— KEY NS 1.5

7

Create two different decimals that have 7 as a digit.

_____

_____

_____

Facts Practice ———————————————— NS 1.0

Write each fraction in simplest form.

1. $\frac{20}{35}$ 2. $\frac{24}{36}$ 3. $\frac{28}{40}$

4. $\frac{12}{48}$ 5. $\frac{16}{40}$

Name _____ Date _____

Equivalent Fractions and Decimals

Write each fraction or mixed number as a decimal.

1. $\dfrac{3}{4}$

2. $1\dfrac{3}{10}$

3. $1\dfrac{2}{5}$

4. $1\dfrac{6}{8}$

5. $2\dfrac{4}{5}$

6. $\dfrac{12}{20}$

7. $1\dfrac{7}{10}$

8. $1\dfrac{2}{4}$

Write each decimal as a fraction or mixed number in simplest form.

9. 0.25

10. 0.4

11. 1.75

12. 1.8

13. 2.5

14. 1.2

15. 3.6

16. 2.9

 **Test Practice**

Write the letter of the correct answer.

17. What is the decimal equivalent of $3\dfrac{2}{5}$?

   A 3.25

   B 3.4

   C 3.2

   D 3.5

18. What is the fraction equivalent of 4.25?

   A $4\dfrac{1}{2}$

   B $4\dfrac{2}{5}$

   C $4\dfrac{1}{4}$

   D $2\dfrac{2}{4}$

Writing Math When you write a decimal as a fraction or mixed number, why is it important to write the answer in simplest form?

_____

_____

_____

_____

_____

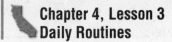
Compare and Order Fractions and Decimals

Problem of the Day ———————————————————— KEY NS 1.2

Bob can mow the lawn in front of his house in 20 minutes. What fraction of an hour, 60 minutes, represents how long it takes Bob to mow the lawn? Simplify.

Number Sense Review ———————————————————— KEY NS 1.2

Write the decimal as a fraction or mixed number in simplest form.

1. 8.6

2. 0.24

3. 4.35

Number of the Day ———————————————————— KEY NS 1.2

2.5

What are some ways you can model 2.5?

_____

_____

_____

Facts Practice ———————————————————— Grade 4 KEY NS 4.1

Find the least common multiple for each group of numbers.

1. 5, 15, 10   **2.** 2, 5, 10

3. 25, 100, 4   **4.** 2, 4, 5

Compare and Order Fractions and Decimals

CA Standard
KEY NS 1.5

Compare. Write >, <, or = for each ◯.

1. $\frac{5}{7}$ ◯ $\frac{3}{5}$

2. $\frac{12}{14}$ ◯ $\frac{6}{7}$

3. $2\frac{7}{15}$ ◯ $\frac{36}{15}$

4. $1\frac{5}{12}$ ◯ $1\frac{5}{6}$

5. $\frac{3}{7}$ ◯ 0.4

6. 0.25 ◯ $\frac{1}{3}$

7. 1.2 ◯ $1\frac{2}{5}$

8. $2\frac{17}{50}$ ◯ 2.35

Order each set of numbers from least to greatest.

9. $\frac{1}{6}$, $\frac{2}{9}$, $\frac{7}{36}$

10. $\frac{23}{50}$, 0.45, $\frac{1}{4}$, $\frac{12}{25}$

11. $\frac{7}{8}$, $\frac{23}{24}$, $\frac{11}{12}$, 0.75

_____   _____   _____

Test Practice

Write the letter of the correct answer.

12. Which statement is true?

A $0.4 > \frac{3}{6}$

B $\frac{9}{6} = 1.3$

C $0.8 > \frac{1}{6} > 1.0$

D $1.5 > \frac{5}{6}$

13. Which statement is true?

A $\frac{2}{5} < 0.2$

B $0.7 > \frac{3}{5} > 0.4$

C $\frac{4}{5} < 0.7 < 0.1$

D $\frac{1}{5} > 0.8$

Writing Math Explain how you could order a group of numbers written as both decimals and fractions.

_____

_____

_____

_____

Mental Math: Fraction and Decimal Equivalents

Problem of the Day
KEY NS 1.5

Troy cut three lengths of fabric. The lengths of fabric are $1\frac{7}{10}$ yards, 1.8 yards, and $2\frac{1}{4}$ yards. List the lengths from longest to shortest.

Number Sense Review
KEY NS 1.5

Compare. Write $>$, $<$, or $=$ in each .

1. $\frac{2}{3}$ _____ $\frac{8}{12}$

2. $\frac{5}{10}$ _____ 0.9

3. $1\frac{3}{4}$ _____ 1.5

Number of the Day
KEY NS 1.5

20

Create one decimal and one mixed number that are greater than 20.

_____

_____

_____

Facts Practice
Grade 4 NS 2.0

Add.

1. $0.5 + 0.4$ **2.** $0.25 + 0.24$ **3.** $0.134 + 0.265$

4. $0.14 + 0.58$ **5.** $0.215 + 0.378$ **6.** $0.431 + 0.36$

Name _____ Date _____

Mental Math: Fraction and Decimal Equivalents

Compare. Write >, <, or = for each ◯**. Use mental math.**

1. $\frac{3}{4}$ ◯ 1.2

2. 0.4 ◯ $\frac{4}{8}$

3. 2.25 ◯ $2\frac{1}{4}$

4. $4\frac{2}{5}$ ◯ 4.2

5. 5.7 ◯ $5\frac{8}{10}$

6. 6.3 ◯ $6\frac{1}{4}$

Use the number line and mental math.

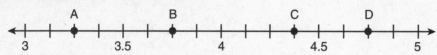

7. Write the fraction represented by point A.

8. What point represents the fraction $4\frac{3}{8}$?

Test Practice

Write the letter of the correct answer

9. Which letter on the number line identifies the location of 2.4?

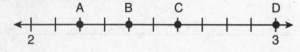

A A

B B

C C

D D

10. Which letter on the number line identifies the location of 3.5?

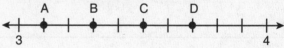

A A

B B

C C

D D

 Writing Math Describe how you can use mental math to compare $1\frac{3}{4}$ to 1.5.

_____

_____

Problem Solving: Field Trip

Problem of the Day

Dora lives $1\frac{3}{5}$ miles from school. Linda lives 1.5 miles from school. Which student lives closer to school?

Number Sense Review

Compare. Write >, < or = for each ⬭. Use mental math.

1. $7\frac{4}{5}$ ⬭ $7\frac{8}{10}$

2. $1\frac{1}{10}$ ⬭ 1.01

3. 5.6 ⬭ $5\frac{5}{8}$

Number of the Day

4.6

Write a mixed number that is greater than 4.6.

_____

_____

_____

Facts Practice ————————————— KEY NS 1.5

Compare. Write >, <, or = for each ⬭.

1. 0.75 ⬭ 0.5

2. $\frac{6}{7}$ ⬭ $\frac{6}{9}$

3. 2.02 ⬭ 2.2

4. $\frac{1}{8}$ ⬭ 0.8

5. $\frac{1}{10}$ ⬭ 0.1

6. 1.378 ⬭ 1.45

Hands On: Algebra and Patterns

Problem of the Day ———————————————— MR 3.3

Karol was growing three flowers from seeds. The first flower grew $3\frac{3}{4}$ inches in one week. The second flower grew $3\frac{1}{2}$ inches. The third flower grew $3\frac{3}{5}$ inches. Which flower grew the most in one week?

Number Sense ———————————————— KEY NS 1.5

Write the decimal form for the unit fraction.

1. $\frac{1}{8}$

2. $\frac{1}{5}$

3. $\frac{1}{4}$

Word of the Day ———————————————— MR 3.3

unit

Find everyday examples for the word unit.

_____

_____

_____

Facts Practice ———————————————— Grade 4 AF 1.1

Find the missing number.

1. $12 + \boxed{} = 20$ **2.** $19 - \boxed{} = 7$ **3.** $\boxed{} + 8 = 17$

4. $26 - \boxed{} = 13$ **5.** $\boxed{} \times 3 = 24$ **6.** $\boxed{} \times 4 = 24$

Name _____ Date _____

Hands On: Algebra and Patterns

CA Standards
KEY AF 1.2, MR 1.1

Draw the next figure in the pattern. Describe the rule.

1. Figure 1   Figure 2   Figure 3

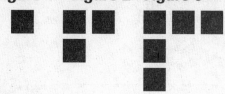

Rule: _____

2. Figure 1   Figure 2   Figure 3

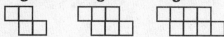

Rule: _____

Figure Number	1	2	3	4	10
Number of Squares	4	6	8		

Test Practice

Circle the letter of the correct answer.

3. Ari was laying stones for a path in his garden. He laid the stones in the pattern shown in Figure 1. Then he added stones to make Figure 2, and added more stones to make Figure 3. What is the rule for this pattern?

Figure 1   Figure 2   Figure 3

A Multiply by 1   **C** Subtract 1

B Add 1   **D** Add 2

4. Emily earns $6 for every hour she is babysitting. What expression could be used to find how much money she would earn in 5 hours?

Hours babysitting	1 hour	2 hours	3 hours	4 hours	5 hours
Amount earned	$6	$12	$18		

A $6 + 5   **C** $6 × 5

B $6 − 5   **D** $6 ÷ 5

Writing Math Using the figure in problem 2, explain how you could find the number of squares in Figure 12.

_____

_____

_____

Name _____ Date _____

Simplify Expressions

Problem of the Day —————————————————————— MR 1.1

Doug created a pattern of towers. Tower 1 was created using 5 blocks.
Tower 2 used 6 blocks. Tower 3 used 7 blocks. Tower 4 used 8 blocks.
What is the rule for the pattern Doug used to build his towers? How
many blocks will be in Tower 20?

Mathematical Reasoning ————————————————————— MR 1.1

Describe the rule for the given pattern.

Figure 1   **Figure 2**   **Figure 3**

Number of the Day —————————————————————— MR 1.1

5

Create a function rule involving the number 5. Then create a function
table using the rule and the input numbers 1, 2, 3, 4, and 5.

_____

_____

_____

Facts Practice ——————————————————————— NS 1.3

Find each value.

1. 10^3 2. 2^3

3. 4^2 4. 8^2

Name _____ Date _____

Simplify Expressions

CA Standards
KEY AF 1.2, NS 1.3

Simplify.

1. $5 + (8 - 6)$ _____

2. $(14 + 2) - 5$ _____

3. $25 + (4 + 20) - 6$ _____

4. $(14 - 12) \times (8 + 4)$ _____

5. $(12 + 6) - 3$ _____

6. $9 + (18 - 9) + 6$ _____

7. $(8 + 2) + (3 + 4)$ _____

8. $(21 - 3) - (4 + 2) + 8$ _____

9. $3 \times 5 - (15 - 5)$ _____

 **Test Practice**

Circle the letter of the correct answer.

10. Joaquin's karate class began with 12 students. Last week 8 more students joined the class. This week 2 times as many students joined the class as last week. Simplify the expression to find how many students are in the karate class now.

$$12 + 8 + (8 \times 2)$$

A 2.4   B 6   C 16   D 36

11. There are 3 people waiting in line to buy movie tickets. Fifteen minutes before the movie starts, 5 times as many people are in line. Ten minutes before the movie starts, 12 more people join the line. Tickets go on sale and 7 people leave the line. Simplify the expression to find how many people are in line now.

$$3 \times 5 + 12 - 7$$

A 4   B 20   C 32   D 38

Writing Math Explain why the expressions $(20 - 4) \times 2$ and $20 - 4 \times 2$ have different values.

_____

_____

_____

_____

_____

_____

Write and Evaluate Expressions

Problem of the Day ———————————————— NS 1.3

When the bus driver began his route, there were 24 passengers. At the first stop, 4 passengers got off at the side door and 3 passengers got off at the front door. At the second stop, 11 passengers got on at the side door and 2 passengers got on at the front door. How many passengers are on the bus after the second stop?

Number Sense ———————————————————— NS 1.3

Simplify.

1. $48 + 4^2 - (1 + 12)$

2. $5 + 3 \times 6$

3. $18 - (6 + 3) \times 2 + 3^2$

Number of the Day ———————————————————— NS 1.3

64

Create a numerical expression that simplifies to 64.

_____

_____

_____

Facts Practice ——————————————————— KEY AF 1.2

Solve.

1. $3 + 2 - 1 =$ ▭   2. $6 + 7 - 3 =$ ▭   3. $12 + 5 - 9 =$ ▭

4. $13 - 5 - 6 =$ ▭   5. $15 - 4 + 6 =$ ▭   6. $28 + 4 - 8 =$ ▭

Write and Evaluate Expressions

Write an algebraic expression for each word phrase. Use the variable _n_ to represent the unknown number.

1. 5 more than 3 times a number.

_____

2. A number to the second power plus 8.

_____

3. 16 minus 2 times a number.

_____

4. A number to the third power minus 5.

_____

5. Twelve plus a number subtracted from 30.

_____

6. 7 less than 4 times a number.

_____

Evaluate each expression when _r_ = 5 and _a_ = 10.

7. $5r - 10$ _____

8 $a + 12 - 3$ _____

9. $r^2 + 12$ _____

10. $3^3 + r$ _____

11. $2^4 + 3r$ _____

12. $(4^2 - r) + 15$ _____

 Test Practice

Circle the letter of the correct answer.

13. Luisa swam _n_ laps at the pool to train for a swim meet. During the next week, she swam 6 times as many laps as she did the first week. During the third week, she swam 6 more laps than she did the second week. If _n_ = 4, what is the value of $6n + 6$?

A 4   **B** 6   **C** 10   **D** 30

14. There are _c_ students in Ray's reading group. There are 5 times as many students in the entire classroom. Then, 12 students leave to go to band practice. If _c_ = 8, what is the value of $5c - 12$?

A 23   **B** 28   **C** 33   **D** 52

 Writing Math Describe different ways to express the equation $x^2 - 5$.

_____

_____

_____

_____

Write and Solve Equations

Problem of the Day ———————————————— KEY

Chris runs a ride at the carnival. He earns $14 an hour and a $50 bonus each day. Write an algebraic expression Chris can use to find the sum of his daily wages. Use the variable x to represent the unknown number.

Algebra and Functions ———————————————— KEY AF 1.2

Write an algebraic expression for each word phrase. Use the variable x for the unknown number.

1. 3 more than a number to the third power

2. 15 less than three times a number

3. the sum of 4 and 9 is decreased by the square of a number

Number of the Day ———————————————————— AF 1.0

7

Write an algebraic expression using x to represent the value of the unknown number. When $x = 1$, the value of the expression should be 7.

_____

_____

_____

Facts Practice ———————————————————————— MR 1.1

Find the value for each variable.

1. $324 + 400 = a$ **2.** $3,000 - 569 = g$

3. $3 \times 561 = y$ **4.** $3,208 \div 8$

Write and Solve Equations

CA Standards
KEY AF 1.2, MR 1.1

Solve and check.

1. $z + 24 = 32$ _____
2. $6m = 48$ _____
3. $d - 37 = 23$ _____
4. $k \div 5 = 22$ _____
5. $g - 72 = 15$ _____
6. $f + 267 = 645$ _____
7. $a \cdot 38 = 570$ _____
8. $m + 623 = 814$ _____
9. $b - 184 = 597$ _____
10. $u \div 13 = 12$ _____
11. $180 = q - 34$ _____
12. $81 + n = 278$ _____
13. $64 \cdot z = 1{,}600$ _____
14. $s \div 56 = 48$ _____
15. $t - 18 = 43$ _____

Choose the equation that represents the situation. Then use the equation to solve the problem.

16. Dan sold 156 tickets in the morning. By the end of the day he had sold 432 tickets. How many tickets did he sell in the afternoon?

    A $156 + n = 432$ **B** $n - 156 = 432$

    _____

17. Alicia gave her friend 6 stamps. She then had 28 left. How many stamps did she have to begin with?

    A $28 - n = 6$ **B** $n - 6 = 28$

    _____

Test Practice

Circle the letter of the correct answer.

18. Larry had 48 stamps. He divided them evenly onto pages in an album. The stamps covered 6 pages in all. How many stamps did he place on each page?

    A 6   **C** 8

    B 42   **D** 48

19. Cassie bought 3 tickets to a play. She paid $27 in all. How much did each ticket cost? Choose the equation that describes the situation.

    A $\$27 \div 3 = \$9$ **C** $\$27 + 3 = \$30$

    B $\$27 \times 3 = 81$ **D** $\$27 - 3 = \$24$

Writing Math Explain how you could use an inverse operation to solve the equation $t - 25 = 12$.

_____

_____

_____

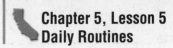
Variables and Functions

Problem of the Day ———————————— KEY AF 1.2

Tara needs to sell 34 tickets to the school play. She has 8 tickets left. How many tickets did Tara sell? Write an equation that represents the situation. Then, use the equation to solve the problem.

Algebra and Functions ———————————— KEY AF 1.2

Tell the inverse operation you would use to solve the equation. Then solve.

1. $x + 12 = 78$

2. $y - 11 = 13$

3. $48 = 16m$

Word of the Day ———————————— KEY AF 1.2

equation

Write an equation for a situation that occurred during your day.

_____

_____

_____

Facts Practice ———————————— KEY AF 1.2

Solve $y = x + 5$ for y, given each value of x.

1. $x = 7$ 2. $x = 12$ 3. $x = 36$

4. $x = 95$ 5. $x = 110$ 6. $x = 47$

Variables and Functions

CA Standards
KEY AF 1.5, AF 1.0

Copy and complete each function table.

1. $y = 5x$

x	y
0	
1	
3	
4	

2. $y = x + 8$

x	y
2	
3	
4	
5	

3. $y = 24 \div x$

x	y
2	
4	
6	
8	

4. $y = 12 - x$

x	y
3	
5	
7	
9	

Circle the letter of the correct answer.

5. Which equation could have been used to create the function table?

x	y
14	22
12	20
10	18

A $y = 2x - 3$

B $y = x + 6$

C $y = 12 \div x$

D $y = x + 8$

6. Marshall made the function table below. What is the value of y when $x = 6$?

x	y
4	11
5	13
6	
7	17

A 12

B 9

C 15

D 17

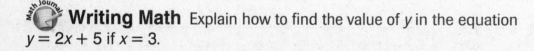 **Writing Math** Explain how to find the value of y in the equation $y = 2x + 5$ if $x = 3$.

_____

_____

Use with text pp. 112–113

Problem Solving: Write an Expression

Problem of the Day ———————————————————— AF 1.0

Lilly drew a pattern. She used information from the pattern to create the table. Write the rule for the function table as an equation with two variables.

x	y
1	3
2	6
3	9
4	12

Algebra and Functions ———————————————————— KEY **AF 1.5**

Use the function table to write an equation.
Then find the value of y for the given value of x.

x	y
10	1
20	2
30	3
40	4

If $x = 1,000$, what is the value of y?

Number of the Day ———————————————————— AF 1.0

19

If the value of x is 19, what is the value of y in the rule $y = 3x + 27$?

_____

_____

Facts Practice ———————————————————— AF 1.0

Find the value of y when x = 10.

1. $15 + x = y$ **2.** $x + 28 = y$ **3.** $78 - x = y$

4. $y = x - 2$ **5.** $y = 3x$ **6.** $40 \div x = y$

Problem Solving: Write an Expression

CA Standards
KEY AF 1.2, MR 2.4

Write an expression to solve each problem.

1. Alexander's Auto World ordered three times as many cars as last year to sell. If Alexander has 10 cars left from last year's inventory of 250 cars, how many cars will Alexander have this year?

   _____

2. Netco Cable charges $34.95 per month for basic cable service, and charges $2.95 per month for each premium channel. If Claire's family decides to add 2 premium channels to their basic service, how much will her family spend per month?

   _____

3. Joe bought a new sleeping bag from an outdoor catalog company. Joe spent $192.90 for the sleeping bag. One-tenth of the cost was added on for shipping and handling. How much was the shipping and handling?

   _____

Test Practice

Circle the letter of the correct answer.

Taxi fares in the city are posted on the door of the taxi. Use the chart to the right to answer both questions.

Initial Charge	$2.70
Cost per Mile	$0.50
Night Surcharge (after 6 PM)	$1.00

4. Jeb takes a taxi to work in the morning. If he travels 8 miles to work, which expression represents the cost of Jeb's taxi ride?

   A $2.70 + (n × $0.50)

   B $2.70 + (n + $0.50)

   C n × $0.50

   D (n × $0.50) − $1

5. Jen and her family traveled 12 miles to a baseball game at 7 o'clock in the evening. What is the cost of the taxi ride to the baseball game?

   A $6.00

   B $7.00

   C $8.70

   D $9.70

Writing Math Define the word variable in your own words. Then explain how variables are used in expressions to solve problems.

Hands On: Model the Distributive Property

Problem of the Day
KEY **AF 1.5**

Sarah knits 5 inches of a scarf in 1 hour. Write an equation that relates the number of inches of a scarf (*i*) Sarah can knit to the number of hours (*h*). Then use the equation to find the number of hours it takes Sarah to knit 25 inches of a scarf.

Algebra and Functions
KEY **AF 1.2**

Find the value of each expression if $a = 5$ and $b = 12$.

1. $25 \div a$

2. $(b - 2) \div a$

3. $(48 \div b) + (a \times 6)$

Number of the Day
MR 1.1

26

How can 26 be written as a sum so that one addend is a multiple of 10?

_____

_____

_____

Facts Practice
Grade 4 KEY **NS 3.0**

Multiply.

1. 7×9 2. 8×7 3. 6×12

4. 11×8 5. 6×7 6. 12×11

Hands On: Model the Distributive Property

Use the Distributive Property to multiply. Show the partial products for each and find the sum. Then write a multiplication sentence for each.

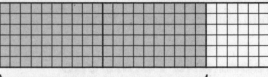

1. 5 × 13 _____   **2.** 6 × 26 _____

_____   _____

_____   _____

Draw and divide a rectangle to show each product.
Use the Distributive Property to find the product.

3. 4 × 24

_____

4. 6 × 12

_____

Test Practice

Circle the letter of the correct answer.

5. Which shows the correct use of the Distributive Property to find the product 8 × 73?

A (8 × 70) 3 (8 × 3)   C (8 + 70) 3 (8 + 3)

B (8 × 70) + (8 × 3)   D 8 + (70 × 3)

6. What value of *y* makes this equation true?

7 × 27 = (7 × 25) + (7 × *y*)

A 7   C 2

B 27   D 3

Writing Math How does dividing a rectangle into two parts model the Distributive Property?

_____

_____

_____

Name _____ Date _____

Use the Distributive Property

Problem of the Day ——————————————————— AF 1.3

Each page of Matthew's coin book holds 24 coins. How many coins can
6 pages hold? Draw and divide a rectangle and use the Distributive
Property to find the answer.

Algebra and Functions ——————————————————— AF 1.3

**Show partial products. Then write a multiplication sentence for finding
the area**

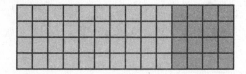

Word of the Day ——————————————————— Grade 4 NS 4.1

factor

Identify the *factors* in the following examples. Then give 3 more examples
of factors.

1. $5 \times 6 = 30$　　　　　　　　　　**2.** $4(3 + 5)$

3. $a + b \times c$　　　　　　　　　　**4.** $(f + g) \times (4 + 7)$

_____

_____

_____

Facts Practice ——————————————————— KEY AF 1.2

Find the value of *x*.

1. $32 = x + 10$　　　**2.** $25 + x = 43$　　　**3.** $x = 16 + 24$

4. $37 = 20 + x$　　　**5.** $x + 29 = 50$　　　**6.** $11 + 19 = x$

Use the Distributive Property

CA Standards
AF 1.3, MR 1.1

Use the Distributive Property to find the value of the variable.

1. $7 \times 64 = (7 \times 60) + (7 \times a)$

_____

2. $5 \times 91 = (5 \times t) + (5 \times 25)$

_____

3. $m \times 49 = (4 \times 35) + (4 \times 14)$

_____

4. $9 \times 34 = (f \times 30) + (9 \times 4)$

_____

5. $6 \times g = (6 \times 80) + (6 \times 5)$

_____

6. $8 \times 78 = (x \times 44) + (8 \times 34)$

_____

7. $5 \times d = (5 \times 13) + (5 \times 14)$

_____

8. $2 \times 95 = (2 \times b) + (2 \times 24)$

_____

Test Practice

Circle the letter of the correct answer.

9. What value of m makes this equation true?

$6 \times 38 = (m \times 30) + (6 \times 8)$

A 30   C 28

B 6   D 3

10. What value of n makes this equation true?

$7 \times n = (7 \times 68) + (7 \times 5)$

A 75   C 73

B 70   D 8

Writing Math How can you use the Distributive Property to find the missing number in the equation: $8 \times c = (8 \times 30) + (8 \times 7)$?

_____

_____

_____

_____

_____

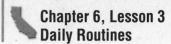
Properties of Addition

Problem of the Day ———————————————————— AF 1.3

Michelle has 9 blue marbles and 4 red marbles. Stephen has 3 times the number of marbles Michelle has. Write two expressions to show the number of marbles Stephen has. Then solve each equation.

Algebra and Functions ———————————————————— AF 1.3

Explain how you can use the Distributive Property to find the value of the variables in:

$6 \times 57 = (n \times 50) + (n \times r)$

Word of the Day ———————————————————— MR 2.1

mental math

Describe how you can use mental math to evaluate each expression.

1. $6 + 14 + 21 + 9$

2. $70 \times 2,000$

_____

_____

_____

Facts Practice ———————————————————— Grade 4 KEY NS 1.2

Compare. Write >, <, or =.

1. 256 ⬭ 250 + 6

2. 109 ⬭ 209

3. 6 + 12 ⬭ 6 + 11

4. 34 ⬭ 10 + 25

Daily Routines

61

Use with Chapter 6, Lesson 3

Name _____ Date _____

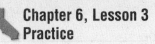

Properties of Addition

CA Standard
KEY AF 1.2, MR 1.1, MR 2.2, MR 2.3,

Evaluate. Identify the property or properties you used.

1. $0 + 73$

_____

_____

_____

2. $(29 + 17) + 61$

_____

_____

_____

3. $76 + r + 24$, given $r = 18$

_____

_____

4. $45 + (65 + m)$, given $m = 0$

_____

_____

Use >, <, or = to make each statement true.

5. $(f + g) + (h + j) \bigcirc (g + h) + (f + j)$

6. $156 + n \bigcirc n + 165$

7. $74 + 27 + b \bigcirc 101 + b$ ____

8. $143 + c \bigcirc 140 + 2 + c$

 **Test Practice**

Circle the letter of the correct answer.

9. If $x = 8$, what is the value of $22 + 16 + x$?

A 46   **B** 40

C 38   **D** 30

10. If $n = 13$, what is the value of $(n + 34) + 36$?

A 47   **B** 70

C 83   **D** 113

Writing Math How can you use addition properties to make it easier to add? Give an example to explain your answer.

_____

_____

_____

_____

_____

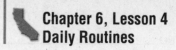

Properties of Multiplication

Problem of the Day ———————————————— KEY **AF 1.2**

Cheryl has 17 baseball cards, 12 soccer cards, and some football cards. Use the Associative Property of Addition to write the sum of these numbers in two ways. Then explain which way you would use if there are 8 football cards.

Algebra and Functions ———————————— KEY **AF 1.2**

Use *n* to write an algebraic expression for each word phrase.

1. a number plus 19

2. 25 divided by a number

3. a number decreased by 7

Word of the Day ———————————————— KEY **AF 1.2**

substitute

Who is a *substitute* teacher? Explain why replacing a variable for a number in an expression or equation is called *substituting*.

_____

_____

_____

Facts Practice ———————————————— Grade 4 KEY **NS 3.2**

Multiply.

1. 15 × 21

2. 113 × 32

3. 28 × 12

4. 64 × 41

Name _____ Date _____

Properties of Multiplication

CA Standard
KEY AF 1.2

Use the properties to complete. Identify each property.

1. $2 \times 56 \times 5 = 2 \times \square \times 56$

2. $50 \times (2 \times 78) = \square \times 78$

_____

_____

_____

_____

3. $3 \times 12 \times 0 = \square$

4. $3 \times 1 \times 20 = 3 \times \square$

_____

_____

Evaluate each expression, given n = 2, r = 5, and s = 6.

5. $4s$

6. $3 \times (n \cdot r)$

7. $7(n \times r) \times 1$

8. $(56 \times s) \times 0$

_____

_____

_____

_____

Compare. Write >, <, or = for each.

9. $(6 \times 8) \times 3 \bigcirc 6 \times 24$

10. $58 \times 1 \bigcirc 59$

11. $17 \times a \times b \bigcirc a \times 17 \times b$

12. $5 \times 28 \times 2 \bigcirc 10 \times 27$

Test Practice

Circle the letter of the correct answer.

13. Which value for x makes this equation true?
    $45 \times 66 = 66 \times x$

    A 20   C 35

    B 45   D 111

14. Which value for t makes this equation true?
    $(8 \times 6) \times 54 = 8 \times (t \times 54)$

    A 2,592   C 48

    B 8   D 6

Writing Math How can you use multiplication properties to make it easier to evaluate an expression? Give an example to explain your answer.

_____

_____

_____

Problem Solving: Field Trip

Problem of the Day ——————————————— MR 1.1

Richard wrote an essay about the Commutative Property of Multiplication. In his essay, he gave $785 \times 1 = 785$ as an example of this property. Is the example correct? Explain why or why not.

Algebra and Functions ——————————————— KEY **AF 1.2**

Complete. Identify the property you used.

1. $60 \times \boxed{} = 60$

2. $2 \times (3 + 4) = (3 + \boxed{}) \times 2$

3. $(2 \times 3) \times 4 = 2 \times (\boxed{} \times 4)$

Number of the Day ——————————————— KEY **AF 1.2**

67

Create an example of the Identity Property of Multiplication using 67 as one factor.

_____

_____

_____

Facts Practice ——————————————— KEY **AF 1.2**

Evaluate, given $a = 5$.

1. $2 \times (a \times 6)$ **2.** $(a \times 10) \times 1$

3. $8a \times 0$ **4.** $3 \times a \times 4$

Hands On: Add and Subtract Fractions with Like Denominators

Problem of the Day
KEY AF 1.2

Mike makes 50 photocopies a day. Use the Associative Property of Multiplication to show two ways to find the number of copies Mike makes in w weeks.

Algebra and Functions
AF 1.3

Find the value of m.

1. $4 \times 56 = (4 \times m) + (4 \times 40)$

2. $(m \times 24) = (9 \times 20) + (9 \times 4)$

3. $(7 \times m) = (7 \times 35) + (7 \times 21)$

Word of the Day
MR 2.3

fraction

What examples of fractions can you use in your everyday life?

_____

_____

_____

Facts Practice
Grade 4 NS 1.5

Write each improper fraction as a mixed number or whole number and each mixed number as an improper fraction.

1. $2\frac{1}{2}$

2. $\frac{15}{3}$

3. $3\frac{4}{7}$

4. $5\frac{1}{8}$

5. $\frac{28}{6}$

6. $\frac{60}{8}$

Name _____ Date _____

Hands On: Add and Subtract Fractions with Like Denominators

CA Standards
KEY NS 2.3, MR 3.2

Find each sum or difference. Write each answer in simplest form.

1. $\dfrac{7}{9} - \dfrac{5}{9} =$ _____

2. $\dfrac{1}{4} + \dfrac{1}{4} =$ _____

3. $\dfrac{5}{8} - \dfrac{3}{8} =$ _____

4. $\dfrac{4}{12} + \dfrac{5}{12} =$ _____

5. $\dfrac{5}{6} - \dfrac{1}{6} =$ _____

6. $\dfrac{9}{10} - \dfrac{4}{10} =$ _____

7. $\dfrac{1}{10} + \dfrac{7}{10} =$ _____

8. $\dfrac{2}{5} + \dfrac{1}{5} =$ _____

9. $\dfrac{1}{5} + \dfrac{3}{5} =$ _____

10. $\dfrac{3}{9} - \dfrac{1}{9} =$ _____

11. $\dfrac{2}{7} + \dfrac{4}{7} =$ _____

12. $\dfrac{2}{3} - \dfrac{1}{3} =$ _____

Test Practice

Circle the letter of the correct answer.

13. Brandon did $\dfrac{2}{6}$ of his homework right after school and $\dfrac{2}{6}$ more after playing lacrosse. How much of his work has he completed?

    A $\dfrac{3}{4}$ B $\dfrac{4}{12}$ C $\dfrac{2}{3}$ D $\dfrac{5}{6}$

14. Mollie is the older of two children so she has $\dfrac{3}{4}$ of the household chores to do. She has completed $\dfrac{1}{4}$ of the household jobs. What part of the jobs must she still do?

    A $\dfrac{1}{2}$ B $\dfrac{1}{4}$ C $\dfrac{2}{8}$ D $\dfrac{3}{4}$

Writing Math Mr. Lee asked his students to wear red, white or blue shirts for their American Revolution unit celebration. $\dfrac{2}{5}$ of the class wore red and $\dfrac{1}{5}$ of the class wore white. Elise thinks that $\dfrac{2}{5}$ of the class had on blue shirts. Is she correct? Tell why or why not.

_____

_____

_____

_____

Name _____ Date _____

Add and Subtract Fractions with Like Denominators

Problem of the Day ——————————————————— KEY NS 2.3

Ben ate $\frac{1}{4}$ of an apple pie. Nancy ate $\frac{2}{4}$ of the apple pie. Use fraction tiles to find the fraction of pie Ben and Nancy ate together.

Number Sense ——————————————————— KEY NS 1.5

Use the number line to write the letter that represents each fraction.

```
     A    B   C   D     E
  <--+--+--+--|--+--+--|--+--+--|--+--+--+-->
     0   1/2  1  1 1/2  2  2 1/2  3  3 1/2
```

1. $3\frac{1}{4}$ **2.** $1\frac{3}{4}$

3. $\frac{1}{4}$ **4.** $2\frac{3}{8}$

Number of the Day ——————————————————— Grade 4, NS 1.5

$\frac{1}{2}$

What examples of $\frac{1}{2}$ can you find around your classroom? In how many ways can you write $\frac{1}{2}$?

_____

_____

_____

Facts Practice ——————————————————— KEY NS 2.3

Use fraction tiles to find each sum or difference.

1. $\frac{1}{4} + \frac{1}{4}$ **2.** $\frac{4}{5} - \frac{2}{5}$

3. $\frac{5}{8} - \frac{2}{8}$ **4.** $\frac{1}{2} + \frac{1}{2}$

Add and Subtract Fractions with Like Denominators

CA Standards
KEY NS 2.3, MR 1.1

Add or subtract. Write each answer in simplest form.

1. $\dfrac{8}{9} - \dfrac{5}{9} =$ ____

2. $\dfrac{2}{5} + \dfrac{2}{5} =$ ____

3. $\dfrac{7}{8} - \dfrac{3}{8} =$ ____

4. $\dfrac{9}{11} - \dfrac{1}{11} =$ ____

5. $\dfrac{5}{8} + \dfrac{1}{8} =$ ____

6. $\dfrac{6}{7} - \dfrac{4}{7} =$ ____

7. $\dfrac{3}{10} + \dfrac{2}{10} =$ ____

8. $\dfrac{1}{12} + \dfrac{2}{12} =$ ____

 **Test Practice**

Circle the letter of the correct answer.

9. Tanya washes $\dfrac{1}{8}$ of the fresh vegetables before lunch. She washes $\dfrac{3}{8}$ of them after lunch. How much of the vegetables were washed?

   A $\dfrac{4}{16}$ B $\dfrac{1}{2}$ C $\dfrac{2}{8}$ D $\dfrac{1}{3}$

10. Blake filled $\dfrac{1}{6}$ of a bowl with blueberries and $\dfrac{3}{6}$ with grapes. What part of the bowl is not filled?

   A $\dfrac{2}{3}$ B $\dfrac{4}{6}$ C $\dfrac{8}{12}$ D $\dfrac{1}{3}$

Writing Math Darcy is doubling a fruit pie recipe which calls for $\dfrac{3}{8}$ cup of kiwi. She figures she will need $\dfrac{6}{16}$ of a cup. Has she figured this correctly? How can you tell?

_____

_____

_____

69

Name _____ Date _____

Hands On: Add and Subtract Fractions with Unlike Denominators

Problem of the Day ———————————————— KEY NS 2.3

Matt needs $\frac{5}{6}$ of a cup of sugar to make a recipe. He has $\frac{4}{6}$ cup. How much more sugar does Matt need?

Number Sense ———————————————— Grade 4 NS 1.5

Tell if the fractions are equivalent. Write *yes* or *no*.

1. $\frac{5}{6}$ and $\frac{10}{12}$

2. $\frac{2}{3}$ and $\frac{4}{9}$

3. $\frac{1}{4}$ and $\frac{3}{9}$

4. $\frac{2}{5}$ and $\frac{14}{35}$

Word of the Day ———————————————— MR 2.3

unlike

Give some examples of things that can be described as *unlike* throughout your school day.

_____

_____

_____

Facts Practice ———————————————— KEY NS 2.3

Add or subtract. Write each answer in simplest form.

1. $\frac{3}{10} + \frac{7}{10}$

2. $\frac{1}{3} + \frac{1}{3}$

3. $\frac{5}{9} - \frac{2}{9}$

4. $\frac{11}{16} - \frac{7}{16}$

5. $\frac{2}{15} + \frac{7}{15}$

6. $\frac{7}{10} - \frac{7}{10}$

Name _____ Date _____

Hands On: Add and Subtract Fractions with Unlike Denominators

CA Standards
KEY NS 2.3, MR 3.2

Find each sum or difference.

1. $\dfrac{1}{3} + \dfrac{5}{9} =$ _____

2. $\dfrac{1}{4} + \dfrac{1}{8} =$ _____

3. $\dfrac{2}{4} + \dfrac{3}{8} =$ _____

4. $\dfrac{2}{3} + \dfrac{1}{4} =$ _____

5. $\dfrac{5}{6} - \dfrac{1}{3} =$ _____

6. $\dfrac{9}{10} - \dfrac{4}{5} =$ _____

7. $\dfrac{1}{2} + \dfrac{2}{5} =$ _____

8. $\dfrac{3}{5} + \dfrac{2}{10} =$ _____

9. $\dfrac{1}{3} + \dfrac{4}{10} =$ _____

10. $\dfrac{2}{3} + \dfrac{2}{8} =$ _____

11. $\dfrac{3}{5} + \dfrac{1}{3} =$ _____

12. $\dfrac{7}{8} - \dfrac{3}{5} =$ _____

Test Practice

Circle the letter of the correct answer.

13. Paige got $\dfrac{3}{4}$ of the problems correct on her math test and $\dfrac{2}{3}$ of the questions correct on her Science test. How much more of her math test was correct?

    A $\dfrac{1}{4}$ 　　　 B $\dfrac{1}{3}$ 　　　 C $\dfrac{3}{12}$ 　　　 D $\dfrac{1}{12}$

14. Bradley wrote $\dfrac{2}{5}$ of his birthday thank-you notes on Saturday and $\dfrac{1}{2}$ of them on Sunday. How many of the thank you notes are completed?

    A $\dfrac{8}{10}$ 　　　 B $\dfrac{9}{10}$ 　　　 C $\dfrac{2}{5}$ 　　　 D $\dfrac{4}{5}$

 Writing Math Lily wants to compare her spelling test scores.
Last week she had $\dfrac{3}{4}$ of the words spelled correctly. This week she
had $\dfrac{7}{8}$ of the words spelled correctly. Which is the better score? Explain.

_____

_____

_____

Add and Subtract Fractions with Unlike Denominators

Problem of the Day ——————————————— KEY NS 2.3

Michelle walked $\frac{1}{4}$ mile to her friend's house. Then she walked $\frac{2}{3}$ miles to the library. Use fraction tiles to find the distance Michelle walked in all.

Number Sense ——————————————— Grade 4 NS 1.5

Find the value for *n*.

1. $\frac{6}{7} = \frac{n}{21}$

2. $\frac{20}{24} = \frac{5}{n}$

3. $\frac{3}{4} = \frac{27}{n}$

4. $\frac{1}{5} = \frac{n}{25}$

Number of the Day ——————————————— KEY NS 2.3

$\frac{1}{4}$

What are some ways to write $\frac{1}{4}$?

_____

_____

_____

Facts Practice ——————————————— KEY NS 2.3

Use fraction tiles to find each sum or difference.

1. $\frac{1}{4} + \frac{1}{2}$

2. $\frac{1}{2} - \frac{1}{6}$

3. $\frac{3}{4} - \frac{1}{3}$

4. $\frac{3}{8} + \frac{1}{2}$

5. $\frac{1}{6} + \frac{2}{3}$

6. $\frac{7}{12} - \frac{1}{6}$

Name _____ Date _____

Add and Subtract Fractions with Unlike Denominators

CA Standard
KEY NS 2.3

Add or Subtract. Write each answer in simplest form.

1. $\dfrac{3}{4} - \dfrac{2}{3} = $ _____   2. $\dfrac{7}{10} - \dfrac{1}{2} = $ _____   3. $\dfrac{5}{6} - \dfrac{5}{8} = $ _____   4. $\dfrac{1}{3} - \dfrac{1}{4} = $ _____

5. $\dfrac{5}{9} - \dfrac{2}{5} = $ _____   6. $\dfrac{11}{12} - \dfrac{1}{8} = $ _____   7. $\dfrac{5}{9} - \dfrac{1}{5} = $ _____   8. $\dfrac{7}{8} - \dfrac{2}{3} = $ _____

9. $\dfrac{3}{10} + \dfrac{2}{5} = $ _____   10. $\dfrac{1}{2} + \dfrac{1}{12} = $ _____   11. $\dfrac{3}{7} + \dfrac{4}{7} = $ _____   12. $\dfrac{1}{3} + \dfrac{2}{5} = $ _____

13. $\dfrac{1}{8} + \dfrac{2}{4} = $ _____   14. $\dfrac{4}{5} + \dfrac{1}{6} = $ _____   15. $\dfrac{2}{9} + \dfrac{2}{3} = $ _____   16. $\dfrac{5}{8} + \dfrac{2}{7} = $ _____

✓ Test Practice

Circle the letter of the correct answer.

17. A roadside farm stand sold $\dfrac{3}{4}$ of their daily harvest of corn on Saturday and $\dfrac{2}{3}$ of their daily pick on Sunday. How much more of the daily pick was sold on Saturday?

   A $\dfrac{1}{3}$ **B** $\dfrac{3}{12}$ **C** $\dfrac{1}{6}$ **D** $\dfrac{1}{12}$

18. The farm stand had $\dfrac{2}{5}$ of a box of beefsteak tomatoes to combine with $\dfrac{1}{4}$ of a box of plum tomatoes. How much of the box was filled with the two kinds of tomatoes?

   A $\dfrac{13}{20}$ **B** $\dfrac{7}{10}$ **C** $\dfrac{3}{9}$ **D** $\dfrac{1}{9}$

 Writing Math A cucumber and a green pepper sat on the farm stand scale. Together they weighed $\dfrac{2}{3}$ of a pound. The farmer took the cucumber off and the scale read $\dfrac{1}{4}$ of a pound. Tell the farmer how to find the weight of the cucumber with the information he has.

_____

_____

_____

Problem Solving: Work Backward

Problem of the Day ——————————————— MR 2.3

Craig walked $\frac{1}{4}$ mile from school to the library. Then, he walked $\frac{2}{5}$ miles home. How far did Craig walk in all?

Number Sense ——————————————— KEY NS 2.3

Add. Write each answer in simplest form.

1. $\frac{1}{3} + \frac{5}{9}$

2. $\frac{1}{3} + \frac{3}{5}$

3. $\frac{3}{7} + \frac{1}{4}$

Number of the Day ——————————————— KEY NS 2.3

$\frac{1}{2}$

Add two fractions so that the sum simplifies to $\frac{1}{2}$. What fractions were added?

_____

_____

_____

Facts Practice ——————————————— KEY NS 2.3

Subtract. Write each answer in simplest form.

1. $\frac{7}{8} - \frac{3}{4}$ 2. $\frac{9}{10} - \frac{2}{3}$

3. $\frac{8}{9} - \frac{1}{2}$ 4. $\frac{5}{6} - \frac{3}{4}$

Name _____ Date _____

Problem Solving: Work Backward

CA Standards
MR 2.6, **KEY** NS 2.3

Use the Work Backward strategy to solve. Explain why your answer makes sense.

1. Noelle was using mulch in her vegetable garden. She used $4\frac{1}{2}$ bags of mulch for three rows of tomato plants. Then, she used $2\frac{3}{4}$ bags of mulch for two rows of pumpkins. Noelle had $3\frac{1}{2}$ bags of mulch left. How much mulch did she have before she used it in her vegetable garden?

2. Sophie bought flour to make a cake and bread. She used $3\frac{3}{4}$ cups of flour to make the bread. She used 1 cup of flour to make the cake. She also made brownies, which used twice the amount of flour she used to make the cake. She had $1\frac{1}{4}$ cups of flour left in the bag. How much was in the bag of flour when Sophie bought it?

 Test Practice

Circle the letter of the correct answer.

3. Jenny lives $\frac{1}{3}$ mile farther from the school than Mike. Nichole lives $\frac{1}{4}$ mile closer to the school than Jenny. Mike lives $\frac{3}{4}$ mile from the school. How far does Nichole live from the school?

A $\frac{7}{6}$ C $\frac{5}{6}$

B $\frac{5}{12}$ D $\frac{1}{12}$

4. Alexandra made taco dip for a party she was going to. She used $\frac{2}{6}$ cup less cheese than beans, $\frac{1}{3}$ cup more tomatoes than cheese, and $\frac{1}{6}$ cup less black olives than tomatoes. If she uses $\frac{3}{4}$ cup of cheese, what amount of black olives does she use?

A $\frac{18}{12}$ C $\frac{10}{12}$

B $\frac{11}{12}$ D $\frac{7}{12}$

Writing Math A picture frame is $\frac{5}{8}$ inch thick. The frame is made of a backing, mat, and glass. The backing is $\frac{3}{16}$ inch thick. The glass is $\frac{3}{8}$ inch thick. How thick is the mat in the picture frame? Explain how you solved this problem.

Use with text pp. 158–159

Hands On: Sums Greater Than 1

Problem of the Day ———————————————————————— KEY NS 2.3

Mrs. Kish has two recipes that she wants to make. The first recipe uses $\frac{1}{3}$ cup of milk. The second recipe uses $\frac{1}{4}$ cup of milk. How much milk does Mrs. Kish need to make the two recipes?

Number Sense ———————————————————————— KEY NS 2.3

Subtract.

1. $\frac{4}{5} - \frac{1}{5}$

2. $\frac{7}{8} - \frac{3}{4}$

3. $\frac{2}{3} - \frac{1}{4}$

Number of the Day ———————————————————————— KEY NS 2.3

$\frac{1}{2}$

What are some fractions that have a sum of $\frac{1}{2}$?

_____

_____

_____

Facts Practice ———————————————————————— KEY NS 2.3

Add. Write each sum in simplest form.

1. $\frac{1}{2} + \frac{1}{3}$

2. $\frac{3}{10} + \frac{1}{5}$

3. $\frac{1}{6} + \frac{3}{4}$

4. $\frac{5}{8} + \frac{1}{4}$

Hands On: Sums Greater Than 1

CA Standards
KEY NS 2.3, MR 2.3

Write the equation illustrated by the model. Write the sum as a mixed number in simplest form.

1.
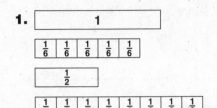

2.
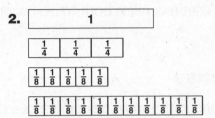

_____   _____

Add. Write each sum as a mixed number in simplest form.

3. $\dfrac{1}{2} + \dfrac{9}{10} =$ **4.** $\dfrac{2}{3} + \dfrac{4}{5} =$ **5.** $\dfrac{3}{8} + \dfrac{3}{4} =$ **6.** $\dfrac{6}{7} + \dfrac{1}{2} =$

_____   _____   _____   _____

7. $\dfrac{3}{4} + \dfrac{7}{8} =$ **8.** $\dfrac{2}{4} + \dfrac{4}{5} =$ **9.** $\dfrac{5}{7} + \dfrac{9}{14} =$ **10.** $\dfrac{11}{12} + \dfrac{5}{6} =$

_____   _____   _____   _____

Test Practice

Circle the letter of the correct answer.

11. A cake recipe calls for $\dfrac{1}{3}$ cup of walnuts and $\dfrac{3}{4}$ cup of almonds. How many nuts are needed in all?

A $1\dfrac{1}{2}$ cups   C $1\dfrac{1}{3}$ cups

B $1\dfrac{1}{12}$ cups   D $1\dfrac{2}{3}$ cups

12. Karyn walks $\dfrac{9}{10}$ of a mile to school, then another $\dfrac{1}{4}$ of a mile to karate classes. How long is her entire walk, expressed in simplest terms?

A $1\dfrac{3}{10}$ miles   C $1\dfrac{3}{20}$ miles

B $1\dfrac{6}{40}$ miles   D $1\dfrac{9}{40}$ miles

 Writing Math How do you know when a mixed number is in simplest form?

_____

_____

_____

Add a Fraction and a Mixed Number

Problem of the Day ———————————————— KEY

A park has two hiking trails. The red trail is $\frac{3}{4}$ mile long and the blue trail is $\frac{7}{10}$ mile long. If Mathew hikes both trails, how many miles will he have hiked?

Number Sense ———————————————— KEY NS 2.3

Write two fractions with unlike denominators that have a sum greater than 1.

Number of the Day ———————————————— KEY NS 2.3

$1\frac{3}{4}$

What are some other ways to write $1\frac{3}{4}$?

_____

_____

_____

Facts Practice ———————————————— KEY NS 2.3

Add. Write the sum in simplest form.

1. $\frac{1}{5} + \frac{9}{10}$ 2. $\frac{3}{4} + \frac{5}{8}$

3. $\frac{5}{6} + \frac{2}{3}$ 4. $\frac{2}{3} + \frac{3}{4}$

Name _____ Date _____

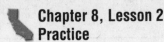

Add a Fraction and a Mixed Number

CA Standards
KEY NS 2.3, MR 2.4

Solve. Write each mixed number in simplest form.

1. $2\frac{5}{4}$ _____

2. $7\frac{4}{8}$ _____

3. $5\frac{7}{5}$ _____

4. $2\frac{18}{10}$ _____

Add. Write each sum in simplest form.

5. $5\frac{1}{8} + \frac{3}{8} =$ _____

6. $\frac{3}{4} + 7\frac{1}{4} =$ _____

7. $3\frac{7}{9} + \frac{5}{9} =$ _____

8. $2\frac{1}{3} + \frac{2}{3} =$ _____

9. $2\frac{1}{3}$
$+ \frac{3}{4}$
_____

10. $\frac{1}{5}$
$+ 4\frac{1}{2}$
_____

11. $\frac{4}{9}$
$+ 1\frac{1}{2}$
_____

12. $7\frac{3}{4}$
$+ \frac{4}{5}$
_____

Test Practice

Circle the letter of the correct answer.

13. What is the sum of $12\frac{2}{3} + \frac{5}{6}$, expressed in simplest form?

A $12\frac{1}{2}$

C $13\frac{1}{6}$

B $12\frac{9}{6}$

D $13\frac{1}{2}$

14. Erik rode his bicycle $5\frac{3}{8}$ miles on Monday. On Tuesday, he rode $\frac{3}{4}$ of a mile further than he did on Monday. How many miles did he ride on Tuesday? Express your answer in simplest form.

A $5\frac{5}{8}$

C $5\frac{9}{8}$

B $6\frac{1}{8}$

D $6\frac{5}{8}$

Writing Math Suppose a problem has the sum $4\frac{18}{12}$. Explain the steps needed to simplify this mixed number.

_____

_____

_____

_____

Add Mixed Numbers With and Without Regrouping

Problem of the Day ——————————— KEY NS 2.3

A family rented two DVDs. One was $\frac{3}{4}$ of an hour long. The other was $1\frac{5}{6}$ hours long. How long did it take the family to watch the two DVDs?

Number Sense ——————————— KEY NS 2.3

What fraction, when added to $2\frac{3}{5}$, gives a sum of $3\frac{1}{10}$?

Word of the Day ——————————— KEY NS 2.3

regroup

Use the objects provided by your teacher to make 2 groups of objects. Then *regroup* the objects into 2 different groups. Discuss the difference between the groups and whether or not any items were lost when the groups were changed.

_____

_____

_____

Facts Practice ——————————— KEY NS 2.3

Solve. Write each mixed number in simplest form.

1. $4\frac{3}{6}$ 2. $2\frac{10}{8}$ 3. $5\frac{7}{6}$

4. $7\frac{3}{9}$ 5. $3\frac{12}{4}$ 6. $1\frac{4}{6}$

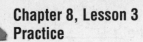
Add Mixed Numbers with and without Regrouping

CA Standards
KEY NS 2.3, MR 2.4

Add. Write each sum in simplest form.

1. $2\frac{4}{5}$
$+ 4\frac{1}{10}$
_____

2. $1\frac{3}{4}$
$+ 1\frac{1}{2}$
_____

3. $5\frac{2}{3}$
$+ 5\frac{5}{6}$
_____

4. $9\frac{1}{4}$
$+ 7\frac{1}{12}$
_____

5. $3\frac{5}{8} + 1\frac{1}{2}$

6. $2\frac{2}{3} + 2\frac{2}{9}$

7. $9\frac{3}{10} + 3\frac{2}{5}$

8. $2\frac{3}{16} + 4\frac{7}{8}$

_____   _____   _____   _____

Evaluate the expression. Write your answer in simplest form.

9. Evaluate $3\frac{1}{2} + y$, if $y = 1\frac{2}{3}$. _____

10. Evaluate $2\frac{3}{4} + y$, if $y = 4\frac{2}{5}$. _____

Test Practice

Circle the letter of the correct answer.

11. What is the sum of $1\frac{2}{5} + 3\frac{7}{10}$, expressed in simplest form?

A $3\frac{11}{10}$ **C** $4\frac{1}{10}$

B $4\frac{11}{10}$ **D** $5\frac{1}{10}$

12. An artist spent $3\frac{1}{2}$ hours painting on Monday, and $5\frac{3}{4}$ hours on Tuesday. How many hours did she paint in all in those two days?

A $8\frac{4}{5}$ **C** $8\frac{4}{6}$

B $9\frac{1}{4}$ **D** $9\frac{3}{4}$

Math Journal **Writing Math** Explain how to evaluate an expression with a variable, when you are given a value for the variable.

_____

_____

Name _____ Date _____

Problem Solving: Field Trip

Problem of the Day ─────────────────────── MR 2.4

Abe walks each day. He walked $4\frac{1}{4}$ miles on Friday and $3\frac{4}{5}$ miles on Saturday. How far did he walk in those two days? Simplify the sum if possible.

Number Sense ─────────────────────── KEY NS 2.3

Add. Write each sum in simplest form.

1. $1\frac{2}{5} + 2\frac{3}{5}$

2. $1\frac{11}{12} + 2\frac{3}{4}$

3. $4\frac{5}{6} + 3\frac{9}{10}$

Number of the Day ─────────────────────── KEY NS 2.3

$4\frac{2}{3}$

Add a mixed number with an unlike denominator to this mixed number and find the sum. Be sure to write the sum in simplest form.

_____

_____

_____

Facts Practice ─────────────────────── KEY NS 2.3

Subtract. Write the difference in simplest form.

1. $\frac{7}{10} - \frac{3}{10}$ **2.** $5 - 2\frac{3}{4}$ **3.** $4\frac{5}{8} - \frac{3}{8}$

4. $\frac{11}{12} - \frac{3}{12}$ **5.** $10\frac{1}{6} - \frac{5}{6}$

Hands On: Rename to Subtract

Problem of the Day

Brooke and Harry built a birdhouse. Brooke worked on the birdhouse for $3\frac{1}{2}$ hours. Harry worked on the birdhouse $\frac{3}{4}$ of an hour longer than Brooke. How much time did it take them to build the birdhouse?

Algebra

Evaluate $3\frac{2}{3} + y$ when $y = 1\frac{1}{2}$.

Number of the Day

3

How can you write 3 as a fraction? Give some examples.

_____

_____

_____

Facts Practice

Add. Write the sum in simplest form.

1. $6\frac{7}{8} + 4\frac{3}{8}$

2. $5\frac{4}{5} + 2\frac{5}{6}$

3. $7\frac{1}{2} + 7\frac{9}{10}$

4. $6\frac{3}{4} + 7\frac{7}{12}$

Hands On: Rename to Subtract

Use fraction tiles to rename the whole number. Subtract the mixed number from the whole number. Sketch your model.

1. $4 - 1\frac{1}{2}$ _____

2. $3 - 2\frac{1}{6}$ _____

3. $4 - 1\frac{2}{3}$ _____

4. $2 - 1\frac{3}{5}$ _____

5. $3 - 1\frac{5}{8}$ _____

6. $2 - 1\frac{1}{10}$ _____

7. $4 - 2\frac{3}{7}$ _____

8. $3 - 1\frac{1}{3}$ _____

9. $4 - 2\frac{9}{10}$ _____

10. Sketch three different ways to show the number 4 as a mixed number.

Test Practice

Circle the letter of the correct answer.

11. Which of the following is equivalent to 3?

A $1\frac{7}{7}$

C $2\frac{5}{7}$

B $2\frac{7}{7}$

D $2\frac{9}{7}$

12. Joel walked 4 miles a day to train for the walkathon. Kevin walked $1\frac{1}{7}$ miles less each day. How far did Kevin walk each day?

A $2\frac{1}{7}$ miles

C $2\frac{5}{7}$ miles

B $2\frac{3}{7}$ miles

D $2\frac{6}{7}$ miles

Writing Math When you use fraction tiles to rename and subtract, how can you check your work? Explain.

_____

_____

_____

_____

_____

Rename to Subtract

Problem of the Day ———————————————— KEY NS 2.3

A roll of ribbon is 6 feet long. Michael cuts off a piece that is $2\frac{3}{4}$ feet long. Jen cuts off a piece that is $1\frac{1}{2}$ feet long. How much ribbon is left on the roll?

Number Sense ———————————————————— KEY NS 2.3

Write a number sentence that shows that the difference of a whole number and mixed number is $4\frac{1}{3}$.

Word of the Day ——————————————————————— NS 2.0

rename

When would you need to rename something in math?

_____

_____

_____

Facts Practice —————————————————————— KEY NS 2.3

Add or subtract. Write the answer in simplest form.

1. $2\frac{1}{4} + 6$

2. $\frac{5}{7} + \frac{1}{2}$

3. $1\frac{3}{8} + 2\frac{1}{4}$

4. $\frac{7}{8} - \frac{3}{8}$

5. $\frac{7}{9} - \frac{1}{3}$

6. $6 - \frac{1}{2}$

Daily Routines

86

Use with Chapter 9, Lesson 2

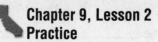

Rename to Subtract

CA Standards
KEY NS 2.3, NS 2.0

Subtract. Check your answer.

1. $\begin{array}{r} 6 \\ - 1\frac{7}{8} \\ \hline \end{array}$

2. $\begin{array}{r} 5 \\ - 3\frac{4}{5} \\ \hline \end{array}$

3. $\begin{array}{r} 3 \\ - 1\frac{3}{20} \\ \hline \end{array}$

4. $\begin{array}{r} 28 \\ - 3\frac{5}{8} \\ \hline \end{array}$

5. $\begin{array}{r} 7 \\ - 4\frac{2}{3} \\ \hline \end{array}$

6. $\begin{array}{r} 6 \\ - 1\frac{4}{9} \\ \hline \end{array}$

7. $\begin{array}{r} 49 \\ - 5\frac{4}{7} \\ \hline \end{array}$

8. $\begin{array}{r} 7 \\ - 4\frac{11}{12} \\ \hline \end{array}$

9. $\begin{array}{r} 8 \\ - 1\frac{3}{4} \\ \hline \end{array}$

10. $\begin{array}{r} 4 \\ - 2\frac{4}{5} \\ \hline \end{array}$

11. $15 - 2\frac{5}{8}$ _____

12. $9 - 7\frac{6}{7}$ _____

13. $38 - 5\frac{3}{5}$ _____

14. $3 - 1\frac{7}{9}$ _____

15. $27 - 2\frac{5}{7}$ _____

16. $4 - 1\frac{5}{12}$ _____

17. $17 - 4\frac{7}{10}$ _____

18. $5 - 2\frac{2}{3}$ _____

Test Practice

Circle the letter of the correct answer.

19. Find $14 - 5\frac{3}{8}$.

 A $8\frac{3}{8}$ **C** $8\frac{5}{8}$

 B $9\frac{3}{8}$ **D** $9\frac{5}{8}$

20. Find $9 - 4\frac{2}{3}$.

 A $4\frac{1}{3}$ **C** $4\frac{2}{3}$

 B $5\frac{1}{3}$ **D** $5\frac{2}{3}$

Writing Math Other than adding, how can you check your
answer to see if it makes sense?

_____

_____

_____

_____

Subtract Mixed Numbers with Like Denominators

Problem of the Day ————————————————————— KEY NS 2.3

A rectangle is 8 feet long. Its width is $3\frac{2}{3}$ feet shorter than its length.
What is the sum of the rectangle's side lengths?

Number Sense ————————————————————————— NS 2.0

Write a number sentence in which the difference of two numbers is $4\frac{3}{8}$.

Number of the Day ————————————————————— NS 2.0

$3\frac{1}{4}$

Write a word problem and expression using the number $3\frac{1}{4}$.

_____

_____

_____

Facts Practice ————————————————————————— KEY NS 2.3

Subtract.

1. $4 - \frac{1}{8}$

2. $3 - 1\frac{3}{5}$

3. $10 - 5\frac{5}{12}$

4. $2 - 1\frac{3}{4}$

Subtract Mixed Numbers with Like Denominators

Subtract. Write the difference in simplest form.

1. $16\frac{4}{11}$
   $-13\frac{9}{11}$

2. $7\frac{3}{5}$
   $-4\frac{4}{5}$

3. $18\frac{1}{10}$
   $-9\frac{3}{10}$

4. $9\frac{2}{7}$
   $-7\frac{6}{7}$

5. $12\frac{1}{4}$
   $-11\frac{3}{4}$

6. $6\frac{2}{19}$
   $-4\frac{7}{19}$

7. $5\frac{7}{15}$
   $-3\frac{7}{15}$

8. $8\frac{1}{5}$
   $-6\frac{2}{5}$

9. $77\frac{2}{9}$
   $-54\frac{4}{9}$

10. $16\frac{3}{4}$
    $-12\frac{3}{4}$

11. $8\frac{1}{7} - 4\frac{3}{7}$

12. $10\frac{1}{8} - 6\frac{3}{8}$

13. $13\frac{1}{9} - 11\frac{3}{9}$

14. $7\frac{4}{6} - 6\frac{5}{6}$

Test Practice

Circle the letter of the correct answer.

15. What is $5\frac{1}{4} - 2\frac{3}{4}$ expressed in simplest form?

    A $2\frac{1}{4}$

    B $2\frac{1}{2}$

    C $2\frac{2}{4}$

    D $3\frac{1}{2}$

16. Carlos wrote $2\frac{4}{5}$ pages of his science paper on Thursday and $4\frac{2}{5}$ pages on Friday. How many more pages did he write on Friday than on Thursday?

    A $1\frac{3}{5}$ pages

    B 2 pages

    C $1\frac{4}{5}$ pages

    D $2\frac{1}{5}$ pages

Writing Math What do you do differently to solve these two subtraction problems: $4 - 1\frac{1}{8}$ and $4\frac{1}{8} - 1\frac{3}{8}$?

_____

_____

_____

Subtract Mixed Numbers

Problem of the Day ———————————————————— KEY **NS 2.3**

Jake is $1\frac{5}{12}$ feet taller than his sister Emma. Jake is $6\frac{1}{12}$ feet tall. How tall is Emma?

Number Sense ————————————————————————— KEY **NS 2.3**

What mixed number is $3\frac{5}{6}$ less than $5\frac{1}{6}$?

Word of the Day ————————————————————————— MR 1.2

common

Give some examples of items that have something in *common*.

_____

_____

_____

Facts Practice ——————————————————————————— NS 2.0

Subtract. Write the answer in simplest form.

1. $3\frac{3}{5} - 1\frac{1}{5}$

2. $6\frac{3}{8} - 2\frac{5}{8}$

3. $5\frac{1}{4} - 4\frac{3}{4}$

4. $7\frac{7}{10} - 1\frac{3}{10}$

Name _____ Date _____

Subtract Mixed Numbers

CA Standards
KEY NS 2.3, NS 2.0

Subtract. Write each difference in simplest form.

1. $2\frac{5}{6}$
    $-1\frac{1}{3}$
    _____

2. $5\frac{3}{4}$
    $-2\frac{1}{2}$
    _____

3. 8
    $-4\frac{3}{10}$
    _____

4. $1\frac{1}{3}$
    $-1\frac{1}{4}$
    _____

5. $9\frac{2}{9} - 7$

6. $12\frac{3}{4} - 8\frac{2}{5}$

7. $10\frac{9}{10} - 5\frac{1}{5}$

8. $4\frac{1}{4} - 2\frac{7}{8}$

_____   _____   _____   _____

Write >, <, or = for the ◯.

9. $6 - 4\frac{3}{5} \bigcirc 4 - 2\frac{7}{10}$ 10. $5\frac{4}{9} - 1\frac{1}{3} \bigcirc 10\frac{2}{3} - 6\frac{1}{9}$ 11. $7\frac{3}{4} - 2\frac{1}{2} \bigcirc 9\frac{7}{8} - 4\frac{2}{3}$

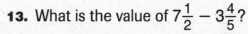 Test Practice

Circle the letter of the correct answer.

12. Elmer made 5 strawberry pies for Thanks-giving dinner, but couldn't resist them. By Thanksgiving Day, he had eaten $2\frac{5}{12}$ of the pies. How many of the pies did he have left?

  A $3\frac{1}{2}$ C $2\frac{3}{4}$

  B $3\frac{7}{12}$ D $2\frac{7}{12}$

13. What is the value of $7\frac{1}{2} - 3\frac{4}{5}$?

  A $3\frac{7}{10}$ C $3\frac{7}{5}$

  B $4\frac{1}{5}$ D $4\frac{3}{10}$

 **Writing Math** Winona and Evan were subtracting $4\frac{1}{4} - 3\frac{1}{6}$. Winona said they should find the common denominator by multiplying 6 × 4. Evan said they should use 12 as the common denominator. Who was correct? Why? Show the subtraction with each of the common denominators.

_____

_____

_____

Use with text pp. 192–195

Problem Solving: Patterns in Tables

Problem of the Day ———————————— KEY NS 2.3

Karen is buying boards for a project. She needs $24\frac{3}{8}$ feet of board. She has $6\frac{1}{2}$ feet already. How much more board does Karen need?

Number Sense ———————————————— NS 2.0

Subtract. Write the difference in simplest form.

1. $8\frac{1}{2} - 5\frac{1}{6}$

2. $6\frac{1}{5} - 3\frac{2}{3}$

3. $4\frac{3}{8} - 3\frac{7}{10}$

Number of the Day ———————————————— NS 2.0

$49\frac{1}{2}$

Throughout your day, find whole numbers or mixed numbers to subtract from $49\frac{1}{2}$. Write the difference in simplest form.

_____

_____

_____

Facts Practice ———————————————— KEY NS 2.3

Add. Write the sum in simplest form.

1. $9\frac{4}{5} + 6\frac{1}{6}$ 2. $2\frac{1}{2} + 3\frac{1}{4}$

3. $5\frac{3}{4} + 2\frac{7}{12}$ 4. $7\frac{3}{8} + 4\frac{2}{3}$

Problem Solving: Patterns in Tables

Find a pattern. Write a function rule to solve. Explain why your answer makes sense.

1. Catrina is making costume skirts for an upcoming school play. She is just finishing a skirt 24 inches long. How long will the skirt be after she hems it?

_____

Catrina's Costume Skirts	
unhemmed length (x)	hemmed length (y)
36 in	$34\frac{1}{2}$ in
$32\frac{1}{4}$ in	$30\frac{3}{4}$ in
$28\frac{1}{2}$ in	27 in
$26\frac{3}{4}$ in	$25\frac{1}{4}$ in

2. Catrina hemmed a skirt that was $25\frac{1}{4}$ inches long after she hemmed it. What was the unhemmed length of the skirt?

_____

Test Practice

Circle the letter of the correct answer.

3. Dominic adds a border to every picture he paints. If he paints a picture $12\frac{1}{4}$ inches wide without the border, how wide will it be after he adds the border?

   A $9\frac{5}{8}$in

   B $14\frac{1}{2}$in

   C $10\frac{1}{2}$in

   D $14\frac{7}{8}$in

Painting with border (b)	Painting without border (p)
$9\frac{1}{8}$ in	$6\frac{1}{2}$ in
$11\frac{3}{8}$ in	$8\frac{3}{4}$ in
$13\frac{1}{8}$ in	$10\frac{1}{2}$ in
$14\frac{13}{16}$ in	$12\frac{3}{16}$ in

4. If Dominic paints a picture $16\frac{3}{4}$ inches wide including the border, how wide was it before he added the border?

   A $12\frac{1}{8}$in

   B $16\frac{3}{8}$in

   C $14\frac{1}{8}$in

   D $19\frac{3}{8}$in

Writing Math Why is it important to test each row in a function table?

_____

_____

Hands On: Multiply Whole Numbers and Fractions

Problem of the Day

Callie is replacing some pipe in her house. She needs $24\frac{2}{3}$ feet of pipe. She has $9\frac{5}{8}$ feet. How much more pipe does she need?

Number Sense

Find the difference.

1. $\frac{5}{11} - \frac{3}{11} = ?$

2. $\frac{2}{3} - \frac{1}{3} = ?$

3. $1 - \frac{7}{8} = ?$

Number of the Day

$\frac{1}{4}$

List some other ways of expressing this amount.

_____

_____

_____

Facts Practice

Simplify.

1. $\frac{3}{5} + \frac{1}{5} = ?$

2. $\frac{1}{2} + \frac{1}{2} = ?$

3. $\frac{4}{9} + \frac{2}{9} = ?$

4. $\frac{1}{8} + \frac{5}{8} = ?$

5. $\frac{7}{10} + \frac{13}{10} = ?$

Name _____ Date _____

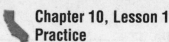

Hands On: Multiply Whole Numbers and Fractions

CA Standard
NS 2.4

Complete the equation represented by each model.
Write each answer in simplest form.

1.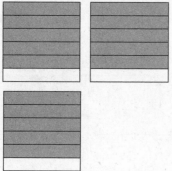

$\square \times \dfrac{\square}{\square}$ _____

2.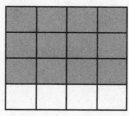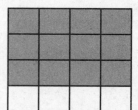

$\square \times \dfrac{\square}{\square}$ _____

Use models to find each product. Write each product in simplest form.

3. $3 \times \dfrac{7}{8} =$ _____

4. $5 \times \dfrac{1}{2} =$ _____

5. $4 \times \dfrac{8}{9} =$ _____

Test Practice

Circle the letter of the correct answer.

6. $7 \times \dfrac{4}{6} =$

A $\dfrac{11}{13}$ C $4\dfrac{5}{6}$

B $\dfrac{28}{42}$ D $4\dfrac{2}{3}$

7. $4 \times \dfrac{2}{5} =$

A $1\dfrac{1}{5}$ C $1\dfrac{3}{5}$

B $\dfrac{8}{20}$ D $\dfrac{6}{9}$

Writing Math Can a whole number multiplied by a fraction give you a product larger than the whole number?

_____

_____

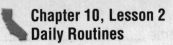

Multiply Fractions

Problem of the Day ———————————————— KEY NS 2.3

Mrs. McGregor ordered 8 pizzas for a class party. The class ate $\frac{3}{4}$ of each pizza. How many whole pizzas were eaten?

Number Sense ———————————————————— KEY NS 1.4

Identify the common factors of the following set of numbers:

12, 18, 36

Number of the Day ———————————————————— MR 2.3

1

Write the number as an equivalent fraction with three different denominators.

_____

_____

_____

Facts Practice ———————————————————— NS 1.0

Divide.

1. 327 ÷ 65   **2.** 378 ÷ 14

3. 786 ÷ 24   **4.** 956 ÷ 68

5. Samantha inflated 125 balloons for a carnival game. How many games can be played if each game takes 7 balloons?

Multiply Fractions

CA Standards
NS 2.4, NS 2.5

Multiply. Write your answer in simplest form.

1. $\frac{1}{5} \times \frac{2}{5} =$

2. $\frac{2}{3} \times \frac{1}{4} =$

3. $\frac{1}{10} \times 2 =$

4. $\frac{3}{8} \times \frac{4}{9} =$

_____ _____ _____ _____

5. $\frac{1}{3} \times \frac{1}{4} =$

6. $\frac{1}{2} \times \frac{6}{12} =$

7. $\frac{16}{20} \times \frac{2}{4} =$

8. $\frac{4}{7} \times \frac{4}{7} =$

_____ _____ _____ _____

9. $6 \times \frac{5}{6} =$

10. $\frac{12}{16} \times \frac{1}{8} =$

11. $10 \times \frac{3}{5} =$

12. $15 \times \frac{2}{3} =$

_____ _____ _____ _____

13. $\frac{1}{2} \times \frac{1}{2} =$

14. $\frac{1}{5} \times \frac{5}{7} =$

15. $\frac{7}{8} \times \frac{8}{9} =$

16. $4 \times \frac{3}{12} =$

_____ _____ _____ _____

Test Practice

17. $\frac{3}{8} \times \frac{9}{12} =$

   A $\frac{9}{32}$ C $\frac{12}{20}$

   B $\frac{12}{80}$ D $\frac{27}{72}$

18. $\frac{2}{9} \times \frac{3}{5} =$

   A $\frac{6}{14}$ C $\frac{5}{14}$

   B $\frac{2}{15}$ D $\frac{5}{45}$

Writing Math Do fractions need to have the same denominator in order to multiply them? Explain.

_____

_____

_____

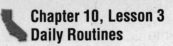
Name _____ Date _____

Multiply with Mixed Numbers

Problem of the Day ———————————————————— NS 2.5

Three fifths of the class has siblings. One fourth of them have sisters.
What fraction of the class has sisters?

Number Sense ————————————————————— KEY **NS 2.3**

Write each improper fraction as a mixed number.

1. $\frac{11}{4}$

2. $\frac{9}{3}$

3. $\frac{22}{3}$

4. $\frac{8}{5}$

Word of the Day ———————————————————— MR 2.3

numerator

Describe the numerator of a fraction in terms of parts and a whole.

_____

_____

_____

Facts Practice ———————————————————— MR 2.6

Multiply. Write your answer in simplest form.

1. $\frac{1}{8} \times 3$

2. $\frac{2}{3} \times \frac{6}{7}$

3. $\frac{3}{4} \times \frac{4}{3}$

4. $\frac{3}{5} \times \frac{4}{7}$

Multiply with Mixed Numbers

CA Standards
NS 2.4, NS 2.5

Multiply. Write each product in simplest form.

1. $1\frac{2}{3} \times \frac{1}{5} =$

2. $\frac{4}{7} \times 3\frac{1}{2} =$

3. $4 \times 2\frac{3}{8} =$

4. $1\frac{5}{6} \times 3 =$

_____ _____ _____ _____

5. $1\frac{2}{3} \times 2\frac{3}{5} =$

6. $2 \times 1\frac{5}{6} =$

7. $4\frac{2}{7} \times \frac{1}{8} =$

8. $1\frac{1}{3} \times 2\frac{1}{4} =$

_____ _____ _____ _____

9. $3\frac{1}{2} \times \frac{3}{5} =$

10. $\frac{2}{5} \times 1\frac{3}{4} =$

11. $1\frac{1}{3} \times 2\frac{5}{8} =$

12. $\frac{4}{5} \times 3\frac{3}{4} =$

_____ _____ _____ _____

13. $5 \times 1\frac{3}{4} =$

14. $1\frac{1}{6} \times 1\frac{2}{7} =$

15. $2\frac{2}{3} \times 2\frac{3}{4} =$

16. $2\frac{1}{4} \times 6 =$

_____ _____ _____ _____

17. $2\frac{2}{5} \times \frac{1}{3} =$

18. $4\frac{2}{3} \times 1\frac{3}{7} =$

19. $4\frac{3}{8} \times 2\frac{1}{5} =$

20. $3\frac{1}{5} \times 2\frac{1}{4} =$

_____ _____ _____ _____

Test Practice

Circle the letter of the correct answer.

21. $3\frac{1}{4} \times \frac{2}{3} =$

  A $1\frac{1}{4}$ **C** $2\frac{1}{6}$

  B $1\frac{1}{6}$ **D** $3\frac{3}{7}$

22. $3\frac{3}{4} \times 2\frac{4}{5} =$

  A $5\frac{7}{9}$ **C** $5\frac{3}{5}$

  B $2\frac{1}{1}$ **D** $10\frac{1}{2}$

 Writing Math Why can you use common factors to simplify?

_____

_____

_____

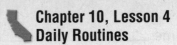
Problem Solving: Field Trip

Problem of the Day ─────────────────────────── NS 2.5

Gina's math class is $1\frac{1}{2}$ hours. For $\frac{2}{5}$ of that time, she will be taking a test.
How long will Gina have to complete her math test?

Number Sense ─────────────────────────── NS 2.4

Multiply. Write each product in simplest form.

1. $\frac{3}{4} \times 1\frac{1}{2}$

2. $2\frac{4}{7} \times 1\frac{2}{9}$

3. $4 \times 3\frac{3}{8}$

Number of the Day ─────────────────────────── NS 2.4

$4\frac{1}{2}$

Find a number during your day to multiply times $4\frac{1}{2}$.
Find the product.

_____

_____

_____

Facts Practice ─────────────────────────── NS 2.4

Write each mixed number as an improper fraction.

1. $2\frac{1}{4}$ 2. $4\frac{7}{8}$

3. $3\frac{1}{3}$ 4. $7\frac{9}{10}$

Hands On: Divide by a Unit Fraction

Problem of the Day ———————————————— NS 2.5

A recipe calls for $\frac{3}{4}$ cup flour. How much flour is needed if the recipe is tripled?

Mathematical Reasoning ———————————————— MR 2.6

Find the product.

1. $3 \times \frac{1}{3}$

2. $9 \times \frac{1}{9}$

3. $7 \times \frac{1}{7}$

4. $4 \times \frac{1}{4}$

Word of the Day ———————————————— MR 2.3

diagonal

Name an object in which its size is determined by measuring its diagonal.

_____

_____

_____

Facts Practice ———————————————— KEY NS 2.2

Divide.

1. $36 \div 9$ 2. $42 \div 7$ 3. $81 \div 9$

4. $78 \div 6$ 5. $128 \div 8$

Name _____ Date _____

Hands On: Divide by a Unit Fraction

CA Standards
NS 2.4, NS 2.5

Match each question with the correct model. Then complete the division sentence.

1. What is 4 divided by $\frac{1}{3}$?

$4 \div \frac{1}{3} = \square$

A

2. What is 4 divided by $\frac{1}{5}$?

$4 \div \frac{1}{5} = \square$

B

3. What is 4 divided by $\frac{1}{2}$?

$4 \div \frac{1}{2} = \square$

C

Complete each division or multiplication to find *a* and *b*. Use fraction strips or grid paper for help.

4. $6 \div \frac{1}{3} = a$ $6 \times 3 = b$ _____

5. $7 \div \frac{1}{5} = a$ $7 \times 5 = b$ _____

6. $8 \div \frac{1}{4} = a$ $8 \times 4 = b$ _____

7. $2 \div \frac{1}{6} = a$ $2 \times 6 = b$ _____

Model with fraction strips.

8. $6 \div \frac{1}{3} =$ _____

9. $8 \div \frac{1}{4} =$ _____

10. $5 \div \frac{1}{2} =$ _____

11. $9 \div \frac{1}{5} =$ _____

12. $7 \div \frac{1}{5} =$ _____

13. $2 \div \frac{1}{6} =$ _____

14. $3 \div \frac{1}{8} =$ _____

15. $4 \div \frac{1}{6} =$ _____

Test Practice

Circle the letter of the correct answer.

16. $6 \div \frac{1}{7} =$

A $\frac{6}{7}$ **C** 6

B $\frac{7}{6}$ **D** 42

17. Beth had 4 feet of rope. She divided each foot into pieces that measured $\frac{1}{4}$ of a foot. how many sections of rope did she then have?

A $\frac{1}{18}$ **C** 4

B 8   **D** 16

Writing Math Explain how to use fraction strips to model dividing a whole number by a unit fraction.

_____

_____

_____

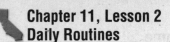
Divide Fractions by a Counting Number

Problem of the Day ────────────────────────── NS 2.5

Twenty-five minutes of playing time makes up half of an indoor soccer game. How many minutes long is the game?

Algebra ──────────────────────────────── KEY **AF 1.2**

Write the value of *n*.

1. $\frac{3}{n} \times 4 = 3$

2. $\frac{n}{6} \times 6 = 4$

3. $\frac{1}{2} \times n = 6$

4. $\frac{5}{n} \times 10 = 10$

Number of the Day ───────────────────────── MR 2.3

8

Create different fractions using an 8 in each one.

_____

_____

_____

Facts Practice ──────────────────────────── KEY **NS 2.2**

Divide.

1. $468 \div 18$ 2. $456 \div 38$

3. $1575 \div 25$ 4. $2242 \div 38$

Divide Fractions by a Counting Number

CA Standards
NS 2.4, NS 2.5

Divide. Write each answer in simplest form.

1. $\frac{2}{3} \div 6 =$ _____
2. $\frac{3}{5} \div 3 =$ _____
3. $\frac{1}{2} \div 8 =$ _____
4. $\frac{1}{4} \div 12 =$ _____

5. $\frac{2}{3} \div 2 =$ _____
6. $\frac{1}{8} \div 9 =$ _____
7. $\frac{4}{3} \div 6 =$ _____
8. $\frac{7}{9} \div 5 =$ _____

9. $\frac{7}{12} \div 21 =$ _____
10. $\frac{3}{5} \div 9 =$ _____
11. $\frac{5}{6} \div 10 =$ _____
12. $\frac{9}{6} \div 3 =$ _____

Complete the function tables.

13. Rule: $y = x \div 4$

x	$\frac{5}{7}$	$\frac{6}{11}$	$\frac{3}{5}$	$\frac{10}{10}$
y				

14. Rule: $y = x \div 6$

x	$\frac{12}{17}$	$\frac{9}{10}$	$\frac{22}{22}$	$\frac{3}{8}$
y				

Test Practice

Circle the letter of the correct answer.

15. Robin has a piece of fabric $\frac{3}{8}$ of a yard long. She needs 2 equal pieces. How long will each piece be?

   A $\frac{3}{16}$ yard   C $\frac{1}{2}$ yard

   B $\frac{3}{4}$ yard   D $\frac{6}{8}$ yard

16. Find $\frac{5}{9} \div 15$.

   A $\frac{1}{27}$ C $\frac{5}{27}$

   B $\frac{3}{9}$ D $\frac{75}{9}$

Writing Math Explain the steps in dividing a fraction by a whole number.

_____

_____

_____

_____

Divide by a Fraction

Problem of the Day ——————————————————— KEY NS 2.3

Tammy is making punch. Her recipe calls for $\frac{3}{4}$ quart of orange juice. The recipe makes 12 servings. How much orange juice is in each serving?

Number Sense ——————————————————————————— NS 2.4

Multiply.

1. $3 \times \frac{1}{6}$

2. $4 \times \frac{1}{2}$

3. $5 \times \frac{1}{5}$

4. $12 \times \frac{1}{6}$

Word of the Day ————————————————————————— MR 2.3

fraction

Where have you used or seen fractions?

_____

_____

_____

Facts Practice ——————————————————————————— NS 1.0

Write the value of n.

1. $\frac{3}{n} \times 4 = 3$

2. $\frac{n}{3} \times 6 = 24$

3. $\frac{1}{2} \times n = 6$

4. $\frac{5}{n} \times 10 = 10$

Name _____ Date _____

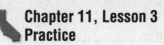
Divide by a Fraction

CA Standards
NS 2.4, NS 2.5

Divide. Write each answer in simplest form.

1. $6 \div \frac{1}{5} =$ _____

2. $\frac{1}{8} \div \frac{3}{4} =$ _____

3. $\frac{1}{5} \div \frac{5}{6} =$ _____

4. $\frac{3}{4} \div \frac{3}{8} =$ _____

5. $4 \div \frac{4}{5} =$ _____

6. $\frac{5}{9} \div \frac{3}{9} =$ _____

7. $\frac{4}{5} \div \frac{1}{4} =$ _____

8. $\frac{1}{4} \div \frac{4}{5} =$ _____

9. $2 \div \frac{2}{3} =$ _____

10. $\frac{7}{8} \div \frac{3}{4} =$ _____

11. $\frac{5}{8} \div \frac{3}{4} =$ _____

12. $\frac{5}{6} \div \frac{1}{3} =$ _____

13. $\frac{2}{9} \div \frac{2}{3} =$ _____

14. $\frac{2}{3} \div \frac{5}{9} =$ _____

15. $\frac{3}{4} \div \frac{1}{2} =$ _____

16. $\frac{5}{12} \div \frac{4}{12} =$ _____

Solve.

17. Tammy had 4 pieces of ribbon. She divided each piece by $\frac{1}{5}$. How many pieces did she have then?

18. Tammy spent $\frac{5}{6}$ of an hour on each of several projects on her own. She spent the same amount of time on each project. She worked for 5 hours. How many projects did she work on?

_____

_____

 Test Practice

Circle the letter of the correct answer.

19. Craig wants to make flash cards out of a strip of paper 3 feet long. He wants each card to be $\frac{1}{4}$ foot long. How many cards can he make?

   A 4   **C** 8

   B 12   **D** 16

20. Find $\frac{3}{8} \div \frac{9}{12}$.

   A $\frac{1}{2}$ **C** $\frac{1}{4}$

   B $\frac{1}{2}$ **D** $\frac{1}{6}$

Writing Math Which is greater: $\frac{4}{5} \div \frac{1}{5}$ or $\frac{4}{5} \div \frac{3}{5}$? Explain your answer.

_____

_____

_____

Divide with Mixed Numbers

Problem of the Day ———————————————— KEY **NS 2.3**

Lila has 8 pieces of ribbon. She divided each ribbon by $\frac{1}{4}$.
How many pieces of ribbon does she now have?

Number Sense ———————————————————— NS 1.0

Write the GCF of each pair of numbers.

1. 9 and 27

2. 11 and 17

3. 12 and 36

4. 18 and 21

Number of the Day ———————————————— MR 2.3

10

What are some different ways to write 10 using fractions or operations
with fractions.

_____

_____

_____

Facts Practice ———————————————————— NS 2.4

Divide.

1. $\frac{4}{5} \div \frac{2}{5}$

2. $\frac{3}{8} \div \frac{5}{12}$

3. $\frac{7}{10} \div \frac{7}{15}$

4. $\frac{5}{9} \div \frac{3}{4}$

Name _____ Date _____

Divide with Mixed Numbers

CA Standards
NS 2.4, NS 2.5

Rewrite each expression as a multiplication expression.

1. $\frac{1}{2} \div 3\frac{1}{4} =$

2. $\frac{7}{8} \div 1\frac{2}{5} =$

3. $2\frac{2}{5} \div 3 =$

4. $2\frac{1}{3} \div 1\frac{1}{4} =$

_____   _____   _____   _____

Write each quotient in simplest form.

5. $3\frac{1}{3} \div 5$ _____

6. $\frac{3}{4} \div 1\frac{4}{5}$ _____

7. $\frac{5}{8} \div 2\frac{1}{4}$ _____

8. $2\frac{2}{3} \div \frac{2}{3}$ _____

9. $4 \div 1\frac{1}{2}$ _____

10. $5\frac{1}{4} \div \frac{3}{8}$ _____

11. $6 \div 2\frac{1}{4}$ _____

12. $3\frac{6}{7} \div 2\frac{1}{4}$ _____

 **Test Practice**

Circle the correct answer.

13. Linda measured $8\frac{2}{3}$ yards of cloth. She then cut it into 4 equal pieces. What was the length of each piece of cloth?

   A $2\frac{1}{6}$yd   C $4\frac{1}{6}$yd

   B $2\frac{1}{3}$yd   D $4\frac{1}{3}$yd

14. Rolf measured $8\frac{1}{4}$ yards of cloth. He then cut it into pieces each measuring $2\frac{3}{4}$ yards. Into how many pieces did he cut the cloth?

   A 2   C 3

   B 4   D 5

Writing Math Is the quotient of a mixed number divided by a mixed number greater than or less than 1? Explain your answer.

_____

_____

_____

_____

_____

Problem Solving: Reasonable Answers

Problem of the Day ———————————————————————— NS 2.5

Marilyn has a piece of lumber that is $2\frac{1}{4}$ yards long. She wants to divide this lumber into 4 pieces of equal length. How long will each piece of lumber be?

Number Sense ———————————————————————————— NS 2.4

Solve. Write each quotient in simplest form.

1. $8\frac{4}{7} \div 3$

2. $2\frac{1}{4} \div 4\frac{1}{2}$

3. $6\frac{1}{8} \div 2\frac{1}{3}$

Number of the Day ———————————————————————— NS 2.4

$2\frac{1}{2}$

Divide this mixed number by a whole number greater than 1. Write the quotient in simplest form.

_____

_____

_____

Facts Practice ———————————————————————————— NS 1.0

Simplify each fraction.

1. $\frac{33}{4}$

2. $\frac{22}{33}$

3. $\frac{30}{3}$

4. $\frac{44}{6}$

5. $\frac{10}{4}$

6. $\frac{17}{5}$

Name _____ Date _____

Problem Solving: Reasonable Answers

CA Standards
MR 2.6, NS 2.5

Tell whether each underlined statement is reasonable or unreasonable. Explain your answer and then solve.

1. Annie has 120 pennies. Fifteen of them are dated before 1960. So, $\frac{7}{8}$ are dated 1960 or later.

_____

_____

2. Joe used $4\frac{1}{8}$ teaspoons of different spices in the soup he was making for dinner. He used about $\frac{3}{8}$ of a teaspoon of each spice. So, he used $1\frac{1}{2}$ spices.

_____

_____

3. Kenny has a large window in the middle of his living room wall. The window is 8 feet long and leaves $\frac{1}{6}$ of the wall at each end. This means the wall is 14 feet long.

_____

_____

 **Test Practice**

Circle the letter of the correct answer.

4. David bought $6\frac{1}{4}$ pounds of ground beef to make hamburgers for his picnic. He used exactly $\frac{3}{4}$ of a pound in each hamburger. How many people got hamburgers?

 A 8 **C** $8\frac{1}{3}$

 B $8\frac{2}{3}$ **D** 9

5. Alexandra has $2\frac{3}{8}$ inches of yarn. How many $\frac{1}{2}$-inch pieces can she cut from it?

 A $1\frac{3}{16}$ **C** $1\frac{3}{4}$

 B $4\frac{3}{16}$ **D** $4\frac{3}{4}$

Writing Math How can you use inverse operations to see if an answer is reasonable?

_____

_____

Hands On: Add and Subtract Decimals

Problem of the Day ——————————————————————— KEY **MG 2.1**

Draw a line segment that is $2\frac{1}{2}$ inches long. If you divide the segment into 5 equal pieces, how long is each piece?

Number Sense ————————————————————————————— NS 1.0

Find the reciprocal of each expression.

1. $\frac{6}{5}$

2. $1\frac{3}{7}$

3. $2\frac{3}{4}$

4. 9

Word of the Day ————————————————————————————— NS 2.0

decimal

Make a list of situations where you would work with decimals.

_____

_____

_____

Facts Practice ————————————————————————————— NS 2.5

Solve. Write each quotient in simplest form.

1. $\frac{4}{5} \div 5 = ?$ 2. $2\frac{1}{4} \div \frac{1}{2} = ?$ 3. $\frac{11}{5} \div \frac{1}{5} = ?$

4. $\frac{9}{4} \div 9 = ?$ 5. $6\frac{3}{4} \div 9 = ?$

Hands On: Add and Subtract Decimals

CA Standards
KEY NS 2.1, MR 2.3

Use models to find each sum.

1. $12.43
    + 8.76

2.   1.987
    + 0.72

3. 67.943 + 18.03 = _____

4. 7.211 + 16.408 = _____

Use models to find each difference.

5.   24.639
    − 3.290

6.   7.338
    − 1.775

7.   89.336
    − 1.951

8. $76.26
    − $67.49

Test Practice

Circle the letter of the correct answer.

9. Baseball legend Ty Cobb averaged 4.875 home runs per season for his career. Hank Aaron averagd 22.255 more per season than Cobb. How many home runs did Hank Aaron average per season?

A 27.821   C 27.13

B 26.27   D 26.103

10. In a study of hummingbirds, researchers found that one adult male hummingbird weighed exactly 3.037 grams. An adult female weighed 3.387 grams. What is the difference in weight between the adult female hummingbird and the adult male hummingbird?

A 6.424   C 6.350

B 0.357   D 0.350

Writing Math Explain how using models helps you to add and subtract decimals.

_____

_____

_____

_____

113
Use with text pp. 254–255

Estimate Sums and Differences

Problem of the Day ———————————————————————————————— KEY NS 2.3

It takes Maria $1\frac{1}{4}$ hours to clean her garage and $\frac{1}{2}$ hour to clean her kitchen. Write the total time she takes to clean as a decimal.

Number Sense ———————————————————————————————————— NS 2.0

Change each decimal to a fraction or mixed number.

1. 0.41

2. 3.25

3. 1.10

4. 0.2

Word of the Day ————————————————————————————————— KEY NS 2.1

hundredths

This word ends with 'ths.' What other words end with 'ths' and why is the ending important?

_____

_____

_____

Facts Practice ————————————————————————————————— KEY NS 2.1

Find each sum or difference.

1. $\frac{1}{5} + \frac{3}{5} = ?$ 	2. $\frac{6}{10} + \frac{1}{2} = ?$ 	3. $\frac{3}{4} - \frac{2}{5} = ?$

4. $\frac{81}{100} + \frac{11}{100} = ?$ 	5. $\frac{1}{2} + \frac{1}{4} = ?$

Estimate Sums and Differences

CA Standards
KEY NS 2.1, MR 2.5

Estimate the sum or difference by rounding each number to the nearest tenth. Check that your answer is reasonable.

1. $0.74 + 0.55 =$ ___

2. $0.48 + 0.32 =$ ___

3. $0.78 - 0.63 =$ ___

4. $0.77 - 0.67 =$ ___

5. $0.637 + 0.85 =$ ___

6. $0.518 - 0.371 =$ ___

7. $0.495 - 0.101 =$ ___

8. $0.17 + 0.18 =$ ___

9. $0.83 - 0.464 =$ ___

10. $0.89 + 0.49 =$ ___

11. $0.67 - 0.209 =$ ___

12. $0.704 - 0.658 =$ ___

Estimate the sum or difference by rounding each number to the nearest whole number. Check that your answer is reasonable.

13. $3.63 + 5.82 =$ ___

14. $16.08 + 9.3 =$ ___

15. $45.927 - 19.83 =$ ___

16. $8.767 - 1.399 =$ ___

17. $\$97.64 - \$43.09 =$ ___

18. $7.79 + 3.011 =$ ___

Test Practice

Circle the letter of the correct answer.

19. In a scale model of the solar system in which the Sun is 1 yard in diameter, Earth would be 107.457 yards from the Sun. Mars would be 199.61 yards from the Sun. To the nearest whole number, estimate how much farther from the Sun Mars would be than Earth.

    A 90 yards   **C** 93 yards

    B 95 yards   **D** 97 yards

20. Marcy took second place in her 100-meter freestyle swimming race, with a time of 57.743 seconds. The first-place swimmer won by 3.36 seconds. To the nearest tenth of a second, estimate the winning time.

    A 54 seconds   **C** 54.3 seconds

    B 54.4 seconds   **D** 56 seconds

Writing Math List several examples of when you might need to make an estimate in real life.

Add and Subtract Decimals

Problem of the Day ——————————————————— MR 2.5

A book costs $3.45 and a box of pencils costs $2.75. Estimate the total
cost of the items by rounding each number to the nearest whole dollar.

Number Sense ——————————————————— NS 2.0

Round each number to the nearest tenth.

1. 5.562

2. 4.234

3. 90.33

4. 0.39

Number of the Day ——————————————————— NS 1.0

20

List different ways to make 20.

_____

_____

_____

Facts Practice ——————————————————— KEY NS 2.1

Find the sum.

1. $34 + 523 = ?$ 2. $762 + 7 = ?$ 3. $45 + 78 = ?$

4. $923 + 198 = ?$ 5. $64 + 9 = ?$

Name _____ Date _____

Add and Subtract Decimals

CA Standards
KEY NS 2.1, MR 2.1

Add or subtract. Check that your answer is reasonable.

1. 7.65
    + 1.95

2. 90.7
    − 61.4

3. 24.9
    − 18.7

4. 7.77
    + 5.55

5. 9.72
    − 5.82

6. 81.0
    + 31.2

7. 63.1
    + 29.9

8. 4.07
    − 3.24

9. 2.653
    + 0.466

10. 8.741
    + 1.199

11. 4.908
    − 0.89

12. 9.001
    − 5.764

13. 14.886
    − 9.902

14. 63.337
    + 21.068

15. 80.015
    + 0.246

16. 4276.9
    − 1582.3

17. $5.008 - 1.867 =$

18. $6.566 + 7.91 =$

19. $4.29 + 6.846 + 17.707 =$

_____   _____   _____

Test Practice

Circle the letter of the correct answer.

20. Collette enjoys designing her own clothes. On Saturday, she purchased 8.542 yd of silk and 17.863 yd of a cotton blend. How many yards of fabric did Collette purchase on Saturday?

    A 15.305 yd   C 16.405 yd

    B 25.305 yd   D 26.405 yd

21. Anthony works part-time at a sub shop. He worked 23.75 hours last week and 15.86 hours this week. How many more hours did Anthony work last week?

    A 7.89 hours   C 7.99 hours

    B 11.11 hours   D 12.11 hours

 **Writing Math** When is it necessary to regroup the ones? Use one of the examples on this page to illustrate.

_____

_____

_____

_____

117
Use with text pp. 258–261

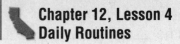
Problem Solving: Field Trip

Problem of the Day ———————————— KEY NS 2.1

Steve walked 0.7 mile on Tuesday, 0.45 mile on Wednesday, and 0.6 mile on Thursday. How many miles did Steve walk in all?

Number Sense ———————————— KEY NS 2.1

Add or subtract.

1. $3.5 - 1.2$

2. $0.68 + 3.561$

3. $5.33 - 4.77$

Word of the Day ———————————— KEY NS 2.1

decimal

Find a situation during your day when decimals are added or subtracted.

_____

_____

_____

Facts Practice ———————————— KEY NS 1.5

Compare. Write, $<$, $>$, or $=$ for each .

1. 7.02 ⬭ 7.20   **2.** 83.74 ⬭ 83.47   **3.** 15.9 ⬭ 14.9

4. 128.8 ⬭ 128.80   **5.** 36.507 ⬭ 36.751   **6.** 22.53 ⬭ 22.52

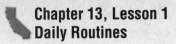
Hands On: Multiply Decimals

Problem of the Day ———————————————— KEY NS 2.1

Juan's dog weighs 12.8 pounds and his cat weighs 6.11 pounds. How much more does the dog weigh?

Number Sense ———————————————— KEY NS 2.1

Round each number to the nearest tenth.

1. 4.76

2. 111.64

3. 45.33

Word of the Day ———————————————— NS 2.0

one-digit number

Give examples of how you might use one-digit numbers during your day.

_____

_____

_____

Facts Practice ———————————————— KEY NS 2.1

Add or subtract.

1. $2.3 + 9.5 = ?$

2. $23.65 + 78.29 = ?$

3. $77.01 - 67.23 = ?$

4. $34.9 - 11.49 = ?$

5. $12.2 + 23 = ?$

Hands On: Multiply Decimals

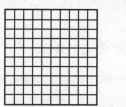

CA Standards
KEY NS 2.1, MR 2.3

Multiply. Use the grids to help solve each problem.

1. 0.2 × 0.8 = _____

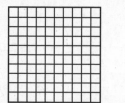

2. 0.4 × 0.8 = _____

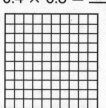

3. 1.2 × 0.5 = _____

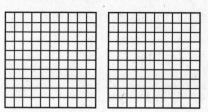

4. 1.2 × 0.7 = _____

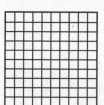

5. 2.6 × 0.4 = _____

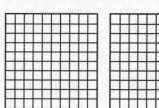

6. 1.5 × 0.9 = _____

Test Practice

Circle the letter of the correct answer.

7. Which expression represents the model?

A 0.5 × 0.6

B $\frac{1}{5} \times \frac{1}{6}$

C 5 × 6

D 0.55 × 0.6

8. Juan can swim three laps in 1 minute. How many laps can Juan swim in 7.5 minutes?

A 2.25

B 225

C 22.5

D 2250

Writing Math How do you solve 0.4 × 0.9 using a decimal grid? Explain.

_____

_____

_____

_____

_____

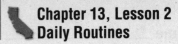
Multiply Whole Numbers and Decimals

Problem of the Day ———————————————————— KEY NS 2.1

One cup of cooked soybeans has 9.6 grams of protein.
How many grams of protein does 4 cups have?

Number Sense ———————————————————————— NS 2.0

Write each money amount as a decimal.

1. 54 cents

2. 3 dollars and 2 cents

3. 7 dimes

4. 11 quarters

Number of the Day ———————————————————— NS 1.1

72

How can 72 be written using different operations?

_____

_____

_____

Facts Practice ———————————————————————— KEY NS 2.1

Find each product.

1. $12 \times 3 = ?$ **2.** $23 \times 4 = ?$ **3.** $54 \times 12 = ?$

4. $88 \times 20 = ?$ **5.** $76 \times 15 = ?$

Daily Routines
122
Use with Chapter 13, Lesson 2

Name _____   Date _____

Multiply Whole Numbers and Decimals

CA Standard
KEY NS 2.1

Find each product.

1. 4.3 × 5 _____   2. 8 × 3.7 _____   3. 2 × 8.1 _____   4. 5.5 × 7 _____

5. 12 × 0.4 _____   6. 1.5 × 8 _____   7. 4 × 0.13 _____   8. 1.8 × 6 _____

9. 4 × 1.22 _____   10. 13.01 × 8 _____   11. 7 × 23.1 _____   12. 4.5 × 25 _____

13. 120 × 0.003 _____   14. 31 × 1.8 _____   15. 1.6 × 23 _____   16. 20 × 0.45 _____

Find a value of *n* to make each statement true.

17. 22 × *n* is between 80 and 85 _____   18. *n* × 85 is between 175 and 250 _____

19. 142 × *n* is between 150 and 280 _____   20. *n* × 77 is between 80 and 150 _____

 **Test Practice**

Circle the letter of the correct answer.

21. Carla ordered 10 beaded necklaces. Each necklace cost $28.59. Which number represents the total cost of the necklaces?

   A $2,859.00   C $28.59

   B $285.90   D $285.80

22. Jackie sold 20 pairs of earrings at the craft fair. Each pair of earrings sold for $15.95. How much money did Jackie receive for all the earrings she sold?

   A $3.19   C $31.90

   B $319   D $3,190

Writing Math Cari bought 2 pins at Carla's Jewelry Shop. Each pin was $18.95. Cari thought the total cost would be $3790. What did Cari do wrong? Explain your answer.

_____

_____

_____

_____

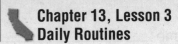

Estimate Products

Problem of the Day ———————————————————— KEY NS 2.1

Brian earns $8 an hour. He worked 6.5 hours on Saturday and 3 hours on Monday. How much did he earn for both days?

Number Sense ———————————————————————— NS 2.0

Estimate the sum or difference by rounding each number to the nearest tenth.

1. $5.67 + 2.45$

2. $0.43 - 0.12$

3. $56.394 - 45.11$

4. $60.99 + 43.06$

Number of the Day ——————————————————————— NS 1.0

30

Throughout the day, find ways that the number 30 is used.

_____

_____

_____

Facts Practice ———————————————————————— KEY NS 2.1

Find the product.

1. $7 \times 100 = ?$

2. $34.1 \times 10 = ?$

3. $0.0003 \times 1,000 = ?$

4. $9 \times 10 = ?$

5. $100 \times 2.9 = ?$

Name _____ Date _____

Estimate Products

CA Standards
KEY NS 2.1, NS 1.1

Estimate each product. Write an equation to show the rounded numbers you used.

1. $36 \times 0.42 =$ _____

2. $15 \times 28.4 =$ _____

3. $0.401 \times 7 =$ _____

4. $7.8 \times 33 =$ _____

5. $175 \times 0.482 =$ _____

6. $92 \times 0.32 =$ _____

7. $2.2 \times 61 =$ _____

8. $518 \times 0.412 =$ _____

9. $35 \times 8.713 =$ _____

10. $0.209 \times 19 =$ _____

11. $3 \times 0.098 =$ _____

12. $38 \times 0.272 =$ _____

13. $11.9 \times 43 =$ _____

14. $25 \times 3.802 =$ _____

15. $308 \times 0.602 =$ _____

 **Test Practice**

Circle the letter of the correct answer.

16. The director of the orchestra drove 321 miles to a concert. She was reimbursed $0.49 per mile. Which is the most reasonable estimate of the amount she will be reimbursed for her mileage?

  A $15   C $160

  B $150   D $1605

17. The assistant director of the orchestra lives 23.25 miles from the concert hall. About how many miles does he drive to and from the concert hall?

  A 56   C 24

  B 46   D 23

Writing Math The director of the orchestra is buying new music for an upcoming concert. The cost of the music before tax is $215. Sales tax is 0.05 of the cost. About how much tax will the director pay on his purchase? Explain whether the actual tax is greater than or less than the estimate.

_____

_____

_____

Name _____   Date _____

Multiply Decimals

Problem of the Day ————————————————— KEY NS 2.1

Mr. Tan travels to and from work 5 times each week. The distance from home to work is 3.6 miles. About how many miles does he travel each week for work?

Number Sense ————————————————————— NS 1.1

Round each number to the nearest hundredth.

1. 5.8924

2. 111.877

3. 0.004

4. 3.555

Word of the Day ————————————————————— NS 1.1

estimate

During the day, when do you need to estimate?

_____

_____

Facts Practice ————————————————————— KEY NS 2.1

Estimate the product.

1. $4.5 \times 32 = ?$ 2. $67.3 \times 0.5 = ?$ 3. $2.75 \times 43 = ?$

4. $2.9 \times 74 = ?$ 5. $28 \times 9.8 = ?$

Multiply Decimals

CA Standard
KEY NS 2.1

Multiply.

1. $0.7 \times 0.4 =$ _____

2. $0.8 \times 0.2 =$ _____

3. $0.5 \times 0.6 =$ _____

4. $0.9 \times 0.9 =$ _____

5. $0.21 \times 3 =$ _____

6. $0.62 \times 0.5 =$ _____

7. $1.8 \times 0.33 =$ _____

8. $0.7 \times 3.5 =$ _____

Choose a value for each variable from the box so that each equation is true.

| 1.04 | 1.4 | 14 | 140 |

9. $n \times 5 = 5.2$ _____

10. $0.8 \times n = 11.2$ _____

11. $n \times 0.42 = 58.8$ _____

Compare. Write >, <, or =.

12. $0.3 \times 0.4 \bigcirc 0.7 \times 0.2$

13. $0.9 \times 0.2 \bigcirc 0.3 \times 0.6$

Test Practice

Circle the letter of the correct choice.

14. Which product shows the correct placement of the decimal point for the problem
7.6×4.82?

  A 3663.2   **C** 366.32

  B 3.6632   **D** 36.632

15. Moonmoney Coffee is on sale for $6.95 a pound. Anna Maria bought 2.25 pounds of the coffee. What was the price of the coffee, not including tax?

  A $15.64   **C** $48.65

  B $62.55   **D** $15.38

Writing Math Explain why $0.7 \times 0.9 \neq 6.3$. Use what you know about multiplying decimals, and state the correct product.

_____

_____

_____

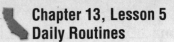
Zeros in the Product

Problem of the Day ———————————————— KEY NS 2.1

Kan buys 4.5 pounds of flour at $0.30 a pound. What is the total cost?

Number Sense ———————————————————— NS 1.1

Write the number.

1. three thousandths

2. twenty hundredths

3. three tenths

4. seventeen hundredths

Number of the Day ———————————————— NS 1.1

0.017

Explain the values of each digit.

_____

_____

_____

Facts Practice ———————————————————— KEY NS 2.1

Find the product.

1. $0.4 \times 0.3 = ?$ 2. $2.1 \times 0.33 = ?$ 3. $4.72 \times 6.8 = ?$

4. $1.5 \times 7.9 = ?$ 5. $2.32 \times 4.5 = ?$

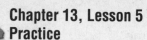
Zeros in the Product

CA Standards
KEY NS 2.1, MR 2.1

Multiply.

1. 0.04
    × 0.5

2. 0.002
    × 6

3. 0.14
    × 0.06

4. 0.025
    × 0.3

5. 0.08
    × 0.09

6. 0.9
    × 0.06

7. 0.42
    × 0.07

8. 0.12
    × 0.09

9. 0.52
    × 0.03

10. 0.77
     × 0.03

11. 0.007
     × 5

12. 0.085
     × 4

Test Practice

Circle the letter of the correct answer.

13. A cowboy hat costs $89.80 in Colorado. The sales tax is $0.03 (3%). How much tax will be charged?

    A $2.47   **C** $2.69

    B $2.49   **D** $2.70

14. The price of a pen is $0.72 at a craft shop in Maryland. The sales tax is $0.05 (5%). What is the total cost of the pen?

    A $0.73   **C** $0.86

    B $0.76   **D** $1.08

 Writing Math Look at the problem in the box.

$$0.08 \times 0.25 = 00200$$

Write the decimal point in the correct place in the product.
Explain.

_____

_____

_____

_____

Problem Solving: Estimate or Exact?

Problem of the Day ———————————————— KEY NS 2.1

A pack of notebook paper costs $1.23. The sales tax where the pack of notebook paper is sold is 0.07 of the purchase price. How much is the sales tax on the pack of notebook paper?

Number Sense ———————————————————— KEY NS 2.1

Multiply.

1. 0.6×0.06

2. 0.6×6.6

3. 0.06×0.06

Number of the Day ———————————————— KEY NS 2.1

0.05

Find the price of any item at a store. If the sales tax is 0.05 of the purchase price, how much is the sales tax on the item you chose?

_____

_____

_____

Facts Practice ——————————————————————— NS 1.0

Multiply mentally.

1. 9×600 2. 900×70 3. 700×800

4. 70×70 5. 80×7 6. 90×300

Name _____ Date _____

Problem Solving: Estimate or Exact?

CA Standards
NS 1.0, MR 2.5

Use the table to solve problems 1–3.

Student Heights	
Student	**Height (in.)**
Mary	58
Stan	64
Leslie	61
Jen	59
Brian	66

1. Sonja made this table to show the heights of some of the students in her class. What is the difference in height between Mary and Stan? _____

2. Which is greater, the difference in height between Leslie and Jen or the difference between Stan and Brian?

_____

_____

3. There are 3 other students in the class with the same height as Leslie. About how many inches are their heights combined?

_____

Use the table of to solve problems 4–6.

Food	Can of Soup	Box of Noodles	Spaghetti Sauce	Jug of Water
Weight	1.2 lbs	0.75 lbs	2.8 lbs	5.25 lbs

4. About how many pounds is the jug of water? _____

5. What is the difference in weight between the spaghetti sauce and the soup? _____

6. About how much would all of the food items weigh all together? _____

Test Practice

Circle the letter of the correct answer.

7. A school fundraiser collected 124,798 canned goods in 5 months. About how many cans did they collect each month?

   A 24,000   c 24,960

   B 25,000   D 25,250

8. A charity raised $15,625 each month for 3 months. How much money did they raise all together?

   A $45,000   c $46,000

   B $46,875   D $46,900

Writing Math A charity raised $167,792 last year. Explain how to use an estimate to find out how much the charity raised each month of the year.

_____

_____

Hands On: Division with Decimals

Problem of the Day ———————————————— KEY NS 2.1

A book costs $9. The sales tax is 0.05. What is the cost of the book with sales tax?

Number Sense ————————————————————— KEY NS 2.1

Write each fraction as a decimal.

1. $\frac{3}{10}$

2. $\frac{2}{5}$

3. $\frac{77}{100}$

4. $\frac{23}{100}$

Word of the Day ————————————————————— NS 2.0

fraction

Explain when you might use fractions in your day.

_____

_____

_____

Facts Practice ———————————————————— KEY NS 2.1

Multiply.

1. $0.2 \times 3 = ?$

2. $0.4 \times 0.5 = ?$

3. $1.2 \times 0.4 = ?$

4. $0.01 \times 122 = ?$

5. $0.25 \times 8 = ?$

Name _____ Date _____

Hands On: Division with Decimals

Use tenths models to divide. Check your answers by multiplying.

1. $6.3 \div 3 =$ _____   **2.** $1.8 \div 6 =$ _____   **3.** $4.2 \div 7 =$ _____   **4.** $1.8 \div 0.3 =$ _____

5. $2.7 \div 9 =$ _____   **6.** $1.2 \div 0.4 =$ _____   **7.** $2.4 \div 2 =$ _____   **8.** $3.6 \div 0.4 =$ _____

Use hundredths models to divide. Check your answers by multiplying.

9. $2.25 \div 0.25 =$ _____   **10.** $81.0 \div 0.90 =$ _____

11. $42.0 \div 0.60 =$ _____   **12.** $20.0 \div 0.05 =$ _____

 Test Practice

Circle the letter of the correct answer.

13. Zachary ran a total of 3.5 miles within a 5-day period. How many miles did he run on average each day?

    A 0.5 miles   **C** 0.7 miles

    B 1.4 miles   **D** 7.0 miles

14. The swim coach asked Ben to swim a total of 2.5 miles before the swim meet. If he swam 0.5 miles a day, how many days did he swim?

    A 3 days   **C** 4 days

    B 5 days   **D** 6 days

Writing Math Explain how dividing decimals is similar to dividing whole numbers.

_____

_____

_____

_____

Name _____ Date _____

Divide Decimals by Whole Numbers

Problem of the Day ————————————————— KEY NS 2.1

Danica divides $4.80 equally among her 3 piggy banks. How much does each bank get?

Number Sense ————————————————————————— NS 2.0

Write each fraction or mixed number as a decimal.

1. $\frac{3}{4}$

2. $11\frac{3}{5}$

3. $\frac{9}{2}$

4. $\frac{10}{5}$

Word of the Day ————————————————————————— NS 1.1

decimals

Give some examples of how decimals are used.

_____

_____

Facts Practice ————————————————————— KEY

Find each quotient.

1. $124 \div 3 = ?$ 2. $55 \div 7 = ?$ 3. $190 \div 6 = ?$

4. $68 \div 5 = ?$ 5. $45 \div 2 = ?$

Name _____ Date _____

Divide Decimals by Whole Numbers

CA Standards
KEY NS 2.1, **KEY** NS 2.2

Find each quotient. Multiply to check your answer.

1. $3\overline{)6.3}$ _____
2. $6\overline{)1.8}$ _____
3. $8\overline{)20.8}$ _____
4. $6\overline{)31.2}$ _____

5. $38.4 \div 4 =$ _____
6. $43.5 \div 5 =$ _____
7. $34.8 \div 6 =$ _____
8. $77.4 \div 9 =$ _____

9. $7\overline{)29.4}$ _____
10. $8\overline{)37.6}$ _____
11. $5\overline{)7.15}$ _____
12. $3\overline{)6.33}$ _____

13. $0.95 \div 5 =$ _____
14. $1.82 \div 7 =$ _____
15. $4.24 \div 8 =$ _____
16. $16.72 \div 4 =$ _____

Insert a decimal point in each dividend to make each equation true.

17. $42 \div 7 = 0.6$

18. $18 \div 3 = 0.06$

19. $301 \div 7 = 4.3$

_____ _____ _____

20. $255 \div 5 = 0.51$

21. $2526 \div 6 = 42.1$

22. $4239 \div 9 = 0.471$

_____ _____ _____

Test Practice

Circle the letter of the correct answer.

23. The relay team ran 12.4 miles. If each of the 4 team members ran the same distance, how many miles did each team member run?

    A 3 miles   C 3.1 miles

    B 3.4 miles   D 4.1 miles

24. Jenny earned $28.20 for babysitting and walking dogs. If each job paid the same amount, how much money did she earn from babysitting?

    A $13.10   C $14.00

    B $14.10   D $14.20

Writing Math When writing a division expression using fractions, why is it important to use the reciprocal of the divisor?

_____

_____

_____

Use with text pp. 296–297

Divide Whole Numbers with Decimal Quotients

Problem of the Day —————————————— KEY

A package of 8 boxes of soup mix costs $4.40. How much is each box?

Number Sense —————————————— KEY NS 2.1

Write each decimal as a fraction and then find the reciprocal of
the fraction.

1. 0.5

2. 0.14

3. 0.75

4. 0.1

Number of the Day —————————————— NS 1.0

28

Write different expressions that give the number 28.

_____

_____

_____

Facts Practice —————————————— KEY NS 2.1

Find the product.

1. $0.7 \times 100 = ?$ **2.** $2.14 \times 0.5 = ?$ **3.** $12.45 \times 10 = ?$

4. $9 \times 0.8 = ?$ **5.** $50 \times 0.33 = ?$

Name _____ Date _____

Divide Whole Numbers with Decimal Quotients

CA Standards
KEY NS 2.1, **KEY** NS 2.2

Write each quotient as a decimal number. Multiply to check.

1. $21 \div 4 =$ _____ **2.** $6 \div 8 =$ _____ **3.** $12 \div 8 =$ _____ **4.** $14 \div 5 =$ _____

5. $4\overline{)9}$ **6.** $8\overline{)7}$ **7.** $5\overline{)38}$ **8.** $15\overline{)3}$

Write each fraction as a decimal.

9. $\dfrac{6}{5}$ _____ **10.** $\dfrac{5}{8}$ _____ **11.** $\dfrac{3}{2}$ _____ **12.** $\dfrac{11}{10}$ _____

 **Test Practice**

Circle the letter of the correct answer.

13. Becky and her sister had $13.00 to spend at the movies. If they split the money equally, how much will they each have to spend?

  A $5.50   **c** $6.00

  B $6.25   **D** $6.50

14. $\dfrac{3}{4}$ of a pizza was left. How can the amount of pizza left be written as a decimal?

  A 0.50   **c** 0.75

  B 1.25   **D** 1.33

Writing Math Explain why 0.25 and $\dfrac{2}{8}$ represent the same number.

_____

_____

Use with text pp. 298–299

Name _____ Date _____

Divide a Whole Number by a Decimal

Problem of the Day ———————————————————— KEY **NS 2.1**

16 people will divide 4 cakes evenly among themselves. How much cake
will each person get? Write your answer as a decimal.

Number Sense ———————————————————————— NS 1.1

Write the reciprocal of each fraction.

1. $\frac{4}{5}$

2. $\frac{15}{20}$

3. $\frac{4}{28}$

4. $\frac{8}{10}$

Word of the Day ———————————————————————— KEY **NS 2.1**

distance

During the day, when do you need to find distance?

_____

_____

_____

Facts Practice ————————————————————————— KEY **NS 2.1**

Find the product.

1. $\frac{4}{5} \times \frac{2}{3} = ?$ 2. $\frac{1}{2} \times 12 = ?$ 3. $15 \times \frac{2}{5} = ?$

4. $100 \times \frac{9}{10} = ?$ 5. $30 \times \frac{5}{6} = ?$

Divide a Whole Number by a Decimal

CA Standards
KEY NS 2.1, KEY NS 2.2

Divide and check.

1. 8 ÷ 0.4 = _____

2. 2 ÷ 0.01 = _____

3. 4 ÷ 0.5 = _____

4. 16 ÷ 0.7 = _____

5. 7 ÷ 0.01 = _____

6. 25 ÷ 0.3 = _____

7. 29 ÷ 0.8 = _____

8. 46 ÷ 0.06 = _____

Circle the letter of the correct answer.

9. Kendall rode her bike 2 miles in 0.8 hour. How fast was Kendall riding?

A 2.5 miles per hour

B 2.0 miles per hour

C 2.2 miles per hour

D 0.5 miles per hour

10. Laura bought 3 gumballs for $0.60. How much did each gumball cost?

A $0.30

B $0.20

C $0.25

D $0.02

Writing Math Explain why you should multiply the divisor and the dividend by the same power of 10.

_____

_____

_____

_____

_____

Name _____ Date _____

Divide a Decimal by a Decimal

Problem of the Day ———————————————————

Kara drives 50 miles in 2 hours. What is her speed per hour?

Number Sense ——————————————————————— NS 1.1

Write the fraction or mixed number.

1. two-thirds

2. five and one-fourth

3. three tenths

4. seven and four hundredths

Number of the Day ——————————————————— NS 1.1

25

Explain when you might use the number 25 during the day.

_____

_____

_____

Facts Practice ——————————————————————— KEY NS 2.1

Find the product.

1. $2 \times \frac{3}{5} = ?$ **2.** $7 \times \frac{1}{10} = ?$ **3.** $\frac{1}{9} \times 6 = ?$

4. $\frac{1}{4} \times 12 = ?$ **5.** $\frac{4}{5} \times 5 = ?$

Divide a Decimal by a Decimal

Divide. Estimate to check that your answer is reasonable.

1. $2.4 \div 0.6 =$

2. $0.25 \div 0.5 =$

3. $17.6 \div 0.4 =$

4. $6.3 \div 0.03 =$

_____

_____

_____

_____

5. $7.2 \div 0.5 =$

6. $8.34 \div 0.4 =$

7. $2.8 \div 0.04 =$

8. $0.02 \div 0.2 =$

_____

_____

_____

_____

Test Practice

Circle the letter of the correct answer.

9. Paul swam 0.24 miles at a rate of 0.8 miles per hour. How long did it take Paul to swim 0.24 miles?

A 0.3 hours

C 0.5 hours

B 30 minutes

D 3 hours

10. Kathryn's fastest time swimming was 1.5 miles in 0.75 of an hour. What was her speed?

A 1 miles per hour

C 1.8 miles per hour

B 2 miles per hour

D 2.2 miles per hour

 Writing Math Explain how to use fractions to solve $1.4 \div 0.8$.

_____

_____

_____

_____

_____

_____

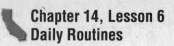
Problem Solving: Use a Simpler Problem

Problem of the Day ———————————————— KEY NS 2.1

Paulos swam 2.2 miles at a rate of 0.5 mile per hour.
How long did it take?

Number Sense ———————————————————— KEY NS 2.1

Find the quotient.

1. $3.32 \div 0.8$

2. $91.85 \div 0.5$

3. $18.5 \div 0.05$

Word of the Day ———————————————————— KEY NS 2.1

divide

Record instances throughout your day in which you divide by
a decimal.

_____

_____

_____

Facts Practice ———————————————————— KEY NS 2.1

Estimate the product.

1. 6.1×4.2 **2.** 1.9×8 **3.** 0.24×0.78

4. 5.1×5.8 **5.** 0.49×0.29

Name _____ Date _____

Problem Solving: Use a Simpler Problem

CA Standards
KEY NS 2.2, MR 2.2

Solve. You can use a simpler problem. Explain why your answer makes sense.

1. Dan has 129 books. This is $1\frac{1}{2}$ times more books than Carmen has. How many books does Carmen have?

   _____

   _____

2. The Denning family drove 221 miles in $4\frac{1}{4}$ hours. What was their average speed?

   _____

   _____

3. While Diana was writing her new novel, she wrote an average of $1\frac{1}{2}$ pages per day. If the novel is 378 pages long, how many days did it take her to write the novel?

   _____

   _____

Test Practice

Circle the letter of the correct answer.

4. Carissa is selling old toys at a yard sale for $0.55 each. She will have to sell 49 to have enough money to buy the new video game she wants. What is the price of the video game?

   A $24.95   C $26.55

   B $26.95   D $89.09

5. Dwayne ran a 12-mile race in $\frac{4}{5}$ of an hour, and then a 10-mile race in $\frac{3}{4}$ of an hour. In which race did he run faster? By how many miles per hour?

   A 12-mile race, by $1\frac{2}{3}$ mph

   B 12-mile race, by $2\frac{1}{10}$ mph

   C 10-mile race, by $1\frac{2}{3}$ mph

   D 10-mile race, by $2\frac{1}{10}$ mph

Writing Math How does using a simpler problem help you figure out which operation to use to solve a problem?

_____

_____

Name _____ Date _____

Hands On: Divide with Multiples of 10, 100, and 1,000

Problem of the Day ———————————————— KEY NS 2.1

Estimate the number of quarters in $16.36.

Number Sense ———————————————————— KEY NS 2.1

Find the product of each.

1. 6×7

2. 50×60

3. 90×400

4. 60×80

Number of the Day ———————————————————— MR 2.3

100

Name three items in your classroom that measure 100 centimeters.

_____

_____

_____

Facts Practice ———————————————————— NS 1.1

Compare. Use >, <, or =.

1. 0.06 __ 0.6

2. 4.82 __ 0.483

3. 0.264 __ 0.246

4. 0.12 __ 0.102

Hands On: Divide with Multiples of 10, 100 and 1,000

CA Standards
KEY NS 2.2, MR 2.2

Use Mental Math to find each quotient.

1. $360 \div 9$

2. $480 \div 60$

3. $21,000 \div 300$

4. $56,000 \div 80$

5. $28,000 \div 7,000$

6. $45,000 \div 500$

7. $160,000 \div 8,000$

8. $240,000 \div 4,000$

9. $400,000 \div 5,000$

10. $50\overline{)4,500}$

11. $200\overline{)800,000}$

12. $3,000\overline{)900,000}$

Use basic facts and patterns to find the quotients.

13. $24 \div 6 =$ _____
$240 \div 60 =$ _____
$2,400 \div 60 =$ _____
$24,000 \div 60 =$ _____

14. $40 \div 8 =$ _____
$400 \div 80 =$ _____
$4,000 \div 80 =$ _____
$40,000 \div 80 =$ _____

15. $56 \div 7 =$ _____
$560 \div 70 =$ _____
$5,600 \div 70 =$ _____
$56,000 \div 70 =$ _____

Test Practice

Circle the letter of the correct answer.

16. There are 2,100 passengers on a cruise ship. If there are 700 cabins, and each cabin holds the same number of people, how many people are in each cabin?

A 3   B 30   C 300   D 400

17. The Greencroft School district ordered 4,260 new computers to divide evenly among the 80 schools. About how many computers will each school receive?

A 5   B 50   C 500   D 800

Writing Math Find the value of n in the equation $4,500 \div n = 90$. Explain how you determined your answer using what you know about division facts and multiples of 10.

_____
_____
_____

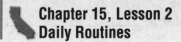
Estimate Quotients

Problem of the Day ————————————————— KEY NS 2.2

Bridget is reading a book that is 360 pages long. If she reads 30 pages each day, how long will it take her to finish the book?

Number Sense ————————————————————— KEY NS 2.1

Multiply.

1. 300×7

2. 9×600

3. 4×500

4. $8,000 \times 7$

Word of the Day ———————————————————— MR 2.3

list

How might a list be helpful today?

_____

_____

_____

Facts Practice ———————————————————— KEY NS 2.1

Divide.

1. $42 \div 7$ **2.** $81 \div 9$ **3.** $78 \div 6$

4. $35 \div 5$ **5.** $72 \div 12$

Estimate Quotients

CA Standards
KEY NS 2.2, MR 2.2

Use compatible numbers to estimate quotients.

1. 841 ÷ 82

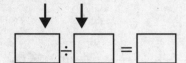

2. 619 ÷ 17

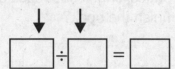

3. 2,485 ÷ 56

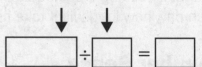

4. 3,129 ÷ 604

5. 48,071 ÷ 764

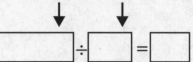

6. 53,903 ÷ 983

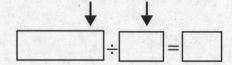

7. 3,214 ÷ 54
_____

8. 46,239 ÷ 87
_____

9. 21,365 ÷ 412
_____

10. 1,011 ÷ 38
_____

11. 1,785 ÷ 21
_____

12. 64,239 ÷ 724
_____

Test Practice

Circle the letter of the correct answer.

13. Jen needs to save $3,192 for a new computer. If she saves $83 per week, about how many weeks will she need to save money?

A 4   **B** 38   **C** 40   **D** 44

14. The music director paid $419.00 for 53 pieces of music. About how much did the director pay for each piece of music?

A $5   **B** $8   **C** $50   **D** $80

Writing Math What is the best estimate for 81,331 ÷ 889? Explain your thinking using what you know about compatible numbers.

_____

_____

_____

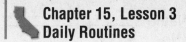
Divide by 2-Digit Divisors

Problem of the Day ———————————————— KEY NS 2.2

Zachary has 388 baseball cards. He places them in album pages that
hold 9 cards each. About how many pages does he need?

Number Sense ———————————————————— KEY NS 2.2

Find the quotients and write any remainders.

1. 723 ÷ 8

2. 81 ÷ 6

3. 49,028 ÷ 7

4. 3,751 ÷ 5

5. 486,054 ÷ 6

Word of the Day ———————————————————— MR 2.3

remainder

Write a sentence using the word remainder to show its meaning.

_____

_____

_____

Facts Practice ———————————————————— NS 1.1

Estimate using front-end estimation. Then estimate by rounding.

1. 79 × 56   **2.** 33 × 28

3. 512 × 43   **4.** 431 × 86

Name _____   Date _____

Divide by 2-Digit Divisors

CA Standards
KEY NS 2.2, **KEY** NS 2.1

Divide. Check your answers.

1. $14\overline{)28}$

2. $26\overline{)130}$

3. $1.5\overline{)16.5}$

4. $32\overline{)9.6}$

5. $4.4\overline{)264}$

6. $55\overline{)660}$

7. $2.4\overline{)5.52}$

8. $16\overline{)65.6}$

9. $77.5 \div 2.5 =$

10. $714 \div 3.4 =$

11. $78 \div 13 =$

12. $3.96 \div 1.2 =$

_____   _____   _____   _____

13. $67.2 \div 32 =$

14. $48.4 \div 4.4 =$

15. $92.8 \div 29 =$

16. $2.24 \div 32 =$

_____   _____   _____   _____

Test Practice

Circle the letter of the correct answer.

17. A sedan gets 32 miles per gallon. If it travels 608 miles, how many gallons of gas does it use?

   A 17   **B** 18   **C** 19   **D** 29

18. There is a car that runs on used vegetable oil. If this car travels 243 miles at 27 miles per gallon, how many gallons were used?

   A 0.9   **B** 9   **C** 19   **D** Not here

Writing Math What is the purpose of adding zeros to the dividend when dividing?

_____

_____

_____

_____

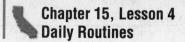
Estimated Quotient is Too Large or Too Small

Problem of the Day ———————————————————— KEY NS 2.2

Mrs. Wilson spent $272 on new bookshelves for her office. If each
bookshelf costs $68, how many did she buy?

Number Sense ————————————————————————— KEY NS 2.2

Divide. Use mental math.

1. 16,000 ÷ 40

2. 5,400 ÷ 90

3. 420,000 ÷ 600

4. 90,000 ÷ 3,000

Word of the Day ———————————————————————— MR 2.3

adjust

When might you adjust something?

_____

_____

_____

Facts Practice ———————————————————————— Grade 4 NS 1.0

Write the value of the underlined digit.

1. 3,648   2. 45,125   3. 378

4. 259,489   5. 17,845   6. 56,489

Estimated Quotient Is Too Large or Too Small

CA Standard
KEY NS 2.2, **KEY** NS 2.1

Divide.

1. $2.4\overline{)38.4}$ _____

2. $16\overline{)288}$ _____

3. $5.2\overline{)130}$ _____

4. $4.4\overline{)2.64}$ _____

5. $12\overline{)1.32}$ _____

6. $34\overline{)289}$ _____

7. $4.2\overline{)63}$ _____

8. $26\overline{)884}$ _____

9. $2 \div 0.32$ _____

10. $328 \div 8.2$ _____

11. $125 \div 0.25$ _____

12. $43.4 \div 6.2$ _____

13. $12.2 \div 4$ _____

14. $18.6 \div 6.2$ _____

15. $283 \div 4$ _____

16. $2.1 \div 4.2$ _____

17. $86.4 \div 0.18$ _____

18. $50.5 \div 2.5$ _____

19. $8.1\overline{)72.9}$ _____

20. $0.93\overline{)37.2}$ _____

21. $0.29\overline{)20.3}$ _____

Test Practice

Circle the letter of the correct answer.

22. Ron is cutting strips of ribbon to go around a quilt. The border is 22.8 meters. Each strip of ribbon measures 0.24 meters. How many strips will he need for the border?

A 94   **B** 95   **C** 97   **D** 107

23. A group of students raised $41.45 on a bottle drive for their field trip. For every bottle returned, they receive $0.05. How many bottles did they return?

A 729   **B** 815   **C** 829   **D** 929

Writing Math How do you know when to adjust the numbers in your quotient when dividing?

_____

_____

_____

_____

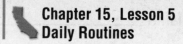

Name _____ Date _____

4- and 5-Digit Dividends

Problem of the Day ———————————————— KEY **NS 2.2**

On the highway, Mrs. Juarez travels at a speed of 65 miles per hour.
At this rate, how long would it take her to travel 520 miles?

Number Sense ———————————————— KEY **NS 2.2**

Multiply or divide.

1. $827 \div 69$

2. $562 \div 40$

3. 79×49

4. $27 \times 1{,}001$

Number of the Day ———————————————— MR 2.3

64

Count to 64 by 4s.

_____

_____

_____

Facts Practice ———————————————— KEY **NS 2.2**

Write +, − , ×, or ÷ to make the sentence true.

1. $3.4 \;\rule{0.6cm}{0.3cm}\; 2.1 = 7.14$

2. $6.14 \;\rule{0.6cm}{0.3cm}\; 2 = 3.07$

3. $5.37 \;\rule{0.6cm}{0.3cm}\; 4.2 = 9.57$

4. $8.88 \;\rule{0.6cm}{0.3cm}\; 4.9 = 3.98$

4- and 5-Digit Dividends

CA Standard
KEY NS 2.1, **KEY** NS 2.2

Divide. Check your answers.

1. $37\overline{)503.2}$

2. $52\overline{)3,848}$

3. $41\overline{)1,230}$

_____ _____ _____

4. $7.3\overline{)66.43}$

5. $2.8\overline{)34.44}$

6. $55\overline{)23,045}$

_____ _____ _____

7. $87\overline{)16,530}$

8. $47\overline{)2,397}$

9. $6.8\overline{)244.12}$

_____ _____ _____

✓ Test Practice

Circle the letter of the correct answer.

10. The California Trail led the gold miners to California. It split from the Oregon Trail and led the settlers to California. If the trail was 12,152 miles in length, and the pioneers traveled in wagons for 98 days, how many miles did they travel each day?

    A 121 **B** 122 **C** 124 **D** 125

11. A gold miner found 2,394 ounces of gold over a 19 day period. If he found the same amount of gold each day, how many ounces of gold did he find a day?

    A 120 **B** 125 **C** 126 **D** 136

Writing Math How is dividing 4- and 5-digit dividends the same as dividing smaller dividends?

_____

_____

_____

Problem Solving: Use the Remainder

Problem of the Day ———————————————— KEY **NS 2.2**

For a documentary Kim was filming, she drove a total of 6,642 miles in 54 days. She drove about the same distance each day. About how many miles did Kim travel each day?

Number Sense ———————————————— KEY **NS 2.2**

Divide.

1. $1,536 \div 12$

2. $10,178 \div 28$

3. $35.46 \div 3.6$

Number of the Day ———————————————— KEY **NS 2.1**

1.5

Find a number throughout your day and divide it by 1.5.

_____

_____

Facts Practice ———————————————— KEY **NS 2.2**

Divide.

1. $827 \div 69$ 2. $562 \div 40$ 3. $249 \div 12$

4. $74 \div 14$ 5. $238 \div 9$ 6. $196 \div 3$

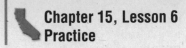
Problem Solving: Use the Remainder

CA Standards
KEY NS 2.2, MR 2.6

Solve. Explain how you used the remainder.

1. Hugh packs oranges for a shipping company. Each packing crate holds 48 oranges. If Hugh has to pack 600 oranges, how many crates does he need?

_____

2. During her vacation, Amy spent $23 on 5 equally priced souvenirs for her friends. What was the price of each souvenir?

_____

3. Mrs. Walker paid $241 for 4 new tires. How much did she pay for each tire?

_____

4. Manuel's family has 3 dogs. Together, they eat 14 pounds of food each week. If their food comes in 5-pound bags, how many bags should Manuel buy to have enough food for 4 weeks?

_____

Test Practice

Circle the letter of the correct answer.

5. Ms. Cartwright can decorate 4 costumes with one yard of trim. If she has to make costumes for 67 students, how many yards of trim should she buy?

   A 15 yards   **C** 16 yards

   B 17 yards   **D** 18 yards

6. Tyra is a part-time dishwasher at a restaurant. Last week, she made $156 for 16 hours of work. What was her hourly pay?

   A $8.75   **C** $9.00

   B $9.25   **D** $9.75

Writing Math Explain why you need to use the remainder to find the answer to problem 4.

_____

_____

_____

_____

Hands On: Model Finding the Mean

Problem of the Day
MR 2.6

Maria made $116 last week working 16 hours at Video Rental. How much does she make per hour?

Number Sense
KEY **NS 2.2**

Divide.

1. $145 \div 8$

2. $21.6 \div 4$

3. $720 \div 0.10$

4. $13.5 \div 0.5$

Number of the Day
MR 2.0

96

List some different ways to express 96.

_____

_____

_____

Facts Practice
NS 2.5

Multiply and simplify.

1. $\frac{2}{3} \times \frac{3}{5}$ 2. $\frac{5}{8} \times \frac{1}{4}$ 3. $\frac{6}{7} \times \frac{14}{15}$

4. $\frac{2}{9} \times \frac{3}{8}$ 5. $\frac{4}{5} \times \frac{6}{10}$

Hands On: Model Finding the Mean

Find the mean of each set of numbers. Use counters.

1. 2, 9, 1, 3, 7, 8 _____

2. 1, 3, 5, 2, 4, 3 _____

3. 6, 9, 7, 9, 8, 9 _____

4. 7, 5, 6, 9, 7, 8 _____

5. 4, 5, 8, 7, 3, 9 _____

6. 1, 2, 6, 1, 7, 7 _____

7. 5, 4, 1, 2, 4, 2 _____

8. 4, 5, 6, 5, 7, 3 _____

Test Practice

Circle the letter of the correct answer.

9. Lorraine spent the following number of hours gardening last week: 1, 4, 1, 2, 3, 1, 2. What is the mean number of hours that Lorraine gardened each day?

A 1
B 2
C 3
D 4

10. Pat found a mean of 4 for her data set. Then she added a number to the data set and found a new mean. Which of these numbers would make no change in Pat's mean?

A 2
B 3
C 4
D 8

Writing Math Explain how to find the mean of this group of numbers.

9, 8, 4, 8, 7, 6, 7

_____
_____
_____
_____

Mean, Median, and Mode

Problem of the Day ——————————————————— SDAP 1.1

Xavier spent the following number of hours playing tennis each day
last week: 3, 2, 2, 5, 3. What is the mean number of hours Xavier spent
playing tennis per day?

Number Sense ——————————————————— KEY **NS 2.1**

Add.

1. $25 + 9 + 7 + 11$

2. $14 + 89 + 35$

3. $108 + 64 + 79 + 57$

4. $27 + 19 + 8 + 30 + 42$

Word of the Day ——————————————————— MR 2.0

average

Give some examples of data that is expressed by averages.

_____

_____

_____

Facts Practice ——————————————————— NS 1.0

Divide.

1. $64 \div 4$ 2. $888 \div 12$ 3. $1,000 \div 50$

4. $405 \div 3$ 5. $256 \div 16$

Mean, Median, and Mode

Use the data in the tables to complete Problems 1–7.

1. What is the mean of the time in hours? _____

2. What is the order of this data set arranged from least to greatest?

Hours Worked
39, 33, 40, 34, 38, 39, 28, 34, 39

_____

3. What is the median of the time in hours? _____

4. What is the mode of the time in hours? _____

5. What is the mean number of miles walked? _____

Miles Walked
3, 3, 5, 9, 8, 4, 3

6. What is the order of this data set arranged from least to greatest?

_____

7. What is the median number of miles walked? _____

Test Practice

Circle the letter of the correct answer.

8. Dave's math grades are 82, 71, 89, 88, 82, and 92. What is his median grade?

   A 82   C 85

   B 84   D 88

9. Danielle picked the following weights of apples; 4 lb, 3 lb, 5 lb, 3 lb, 6 lb, and 3 lb. What is the mean weight of the apples?

   A 3 lb   C 4 lb

   B 5 lb   D 6 lb

Writing Math Out of the mean, median, and mode, which one does a data set NOT have to have?

_____

_____

_____

Line Graphs

Problem of the Day —————————————————— SDAP 1.1

In his last 7 swim practices Zeke swam 25, 33, 41, 26, 30, 33, and 36 laps. What is the mean, median, and mode of this data set?

Statistics, Data Analysis, and Probability ——————— SDAP 1.1

List the numbers in order from least to greatest.

1. 25, 16, 38, 9, 12, 17

2. 14, 182, 104, 128, 72, 77, 41

3. 90, 51, 153, 101, 88, 135, 217

Word of the Day —————————————————————— MR 2.3

graph

Give some examples of the kinds of data that can be represented on graphs.

_____

_____

_____

Facts Practice ——————————————————————— KEY NS 2.1

Multiply.

1. 90×6 **2.** $2,000 \times 8$ **3.** 50×400

4. $7,000 \times 5$ **5.** $8,000 \times 8$

Name _____ Date _____

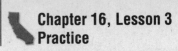
Make Line Graphs

CA Standard
KEY SDAP 1.4

Use the table for Problem 1.

Gallons of Orange Juice Sold							
Time	9:00	10:00	11:00	12:00	1:00	2:00	3:00
Gallons	0	2	2	3	4	5	6

1. Use the Gallons of Orange Juice Sold data to make a line graph.

Use the line graph for Problems 2–3 and Writing Math.

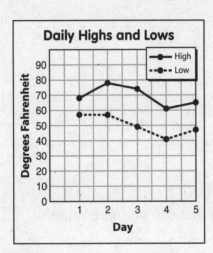

Test Practice

Circle the letter of the correct answer.

2. What were the approximate high and low temperatures on Day 2?

A High 78°, Low 58°   C High 72°, Low 48°

B High 60°, Low 58°   D High 58°, Low 78°

3. Between which two days was there an increase in both the high and low temperatures?

A Day 1–2   C Day 2–3

B Day 3–4   D Day 4–5

Writing Math Use the "Daily Highs and Lows" line graph above to make a generalization about temperature change in the area where the temperatures were collected. About how much does the temperature change on a typical day?

_____

_____

Name _____ Date _____

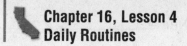

Chapter 16, Lesson 4
Daily Routines

Circle Graphs

Problem of the Day ———————————————— SDAP 1.2

Sergio observed the number of birds at two different bird feeders over 6 weeks. He then created a double line graph to record his data. What labels should he use on his graph?

Measurement and Geometry ———————————— Grade 4 KEY MG 2.0

Use Workmat 7 and plot the ordered pairs.

1. $(2, 5)$

2. $(5, 2)$

3. $(6, 0)$

4. $(0, 6)$

Number of the Day ———————————————————— MR 2.3

360

What number is half of 360?

_____

_____

_____

Facts Practice ———————————————————————— NS 2.5

Multiply.

1. $360 \times \frac{1}{4}$

2. $360 \times \frac{11}{12}$

3. $360 \times \frac{1}{3}$

4. $\frac{5}{8} \times 360$

5. $\frac{1}{10} \times 360$

Name _____ Date _____

Circle Graphs

CA Standards
AF 1.1, SDAP 1.2

Use the circle graph to answer Problems 1–3.

Jillian's class took a nature walk and kept track of the
different types of trees they found. The circle graph
shows the different types of trees the class found.

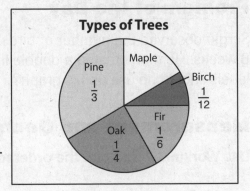

Types of Trees

1. What fraction of the trees
   Jillian'sclass counted were maples? _____

2. What fraction of the trees were pines or firs? _____

3. If the class counted 84 trees in all, how many of
   them were birches? _____

Test Practice

**Use the circle graph to answer Problems
4–5 and Writing Math.**

Circle the letter of the correct answer.

4. Erin organized her book collection into five
   different categories. The circle graph shows the
   fraction of her entire collection represented by
   each category. What fraction of her books are
   about photography?

   A $\frac{1}{10}$ **C** $\frac{1}{5}$

   B $\frac{1}{4}$ **D** $\frac{1}{3}$

Erin's Books

5. Erin has 80 books in all. How many of them are biographies?

   A 5   **B** 10   **C** 16   **D** 20

 Writing Math Why would it be impossible for the total number of
Erin's books to be 95? What number besides 80 would be possible for the total
number of Erin's books? Explain and give an example.

_____

_____

_____

_____

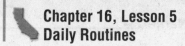
Histograms

Problem of the Day ────────────────────────── SDAP 1.2

Maria is looking at a circle graph of how many hours students spend on homework per night. She notices that $\frac{1}{8}$ of the graph shows half an hour, $\frac{3}{8}$ shows 1 hour, $\frac{1}{4}$ shows $1\frac{1}{2}$ hours and $\frac{1}{8}$ shows more than 2 hours. If 32 people were surveyed, how many spent 1 hour on homework?

Algebra and Functions ──────────────────── KEY **AF 1.4**

The graph shows how Lorena spent her 2 hours at soccer practice.

1. How many minutes were spent on a scrimmage?

2. How many more minutes were spent on drills than running laps?

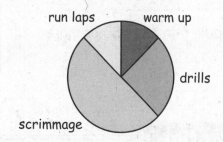

Soccer Practice

run laps warm up

drills

scrimmage

Number of the Day ──────────────────────────── MR 2.0

12

What are some items that come in packages of 12?

_____

_____

_____

Facts Practice ──────────────────────────── KEY **NS 2.1**

Add.

1. $96 + 125$ **2.** $2,145 + 454$ **3.** $516 + 741$

Histograms

CA Standards
SDAP 1.2, AF 1.1

Use the histogram for Problems 1–3.

The histogram shows the amount of money in dollars that people donated to a fund to help save the whales.

1. How many people donated between $50 and $59?

_____

2. For which interval did the most people donate money to the fund?

_____

3. How many people donated $50 or more to the fund?

_____

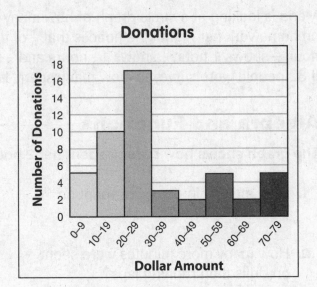

Donations

Test Practice

Circle the letter of the correct answer.

6. Andy surveyed the people in his building to find out their ages. His results are shown below. Which of the following is the best choice for intervals for a histogram?

2, 65, 10, 6, 37, 41, 68, 52, 49, 18, 21

A 1–20, 21–40, 41–50, 51–60
C 1–15, 16–30, 31–45, 46–60, 61–65
B 1–20, 21–40, 41–50, 51–60, 61–70
D 1–25, 26–50, 51–75, 75–100

7. If the "Donations" histogram above was redone using the intervals 0–19, 20–39, 40–59, and 60–79, which interval would have the most donations?

A 0–19   B 20–39   C 40–59   D 60–79

 Writing Math How can a histogram be useful? When is it most useful?

_____

_____

Name _____ Date _____

Problem Solving: Choose an Appropriate Graph

Problem of the Day ———————————————————— SDAP 1.2

Athletes on one sports team traveled the following number of miles to their games this season: 8, 9, 2, 4, 4, 3, 6, 11, 12, 5, 2, 7, 13, 15, and 1. The team's coach wants to make a histogram to display this data. What intervals could he use for the histogram?

Algebra and Functions ——————————————————— AF 1.1

For Exercises 1–2, use the histogram.

1. How many times did the team have to travel between 4 and 7 miles to a game?

2. Did the team travel to more games that were 8 to 11 miles away or 0 to 3 miles away?

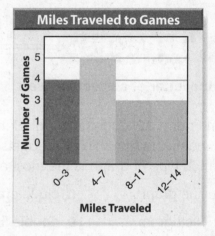

Word of the Day ——————————————————————— SDAP 1.2

histogram

Look through a newspaper to find an example of a histogram. Share with the class.

_____

_____

_____

Facts Practice ———————————————————— Grade 4 AF 1.1

Solve each equation.

1. $90 \times 6 = a$ 2. $2,000 \times 8 = t$ 3. $50 \times 400 = p$

4. $7,000 \times 5 = y$ 5. $8 \times 8,000 = j$

Choose an Appropriate Graph

CA Standards
MR 2.3, SDAP 1.2

Use a graph to display the data set. Explain your choice of graph.

1.

Water Temperatures at the Beach					
Day	Thurs.	Fri.	Sat.	Sun	Mon
Temp.(°F)	65	60	52	63	70

 Test Practice

Circle the letter of correct answer.

2. On Friday, 12 students bought lunch. Seven students bought pizza, 3
   students bought chicken nuggets, and 2 students bought a chef salad.
   Which type of graph is the most appropriate to display the data?

   A line graph   C circle graph

   B histogram   D double line graph

3. There were 63 students who bought their lunch in all. On Monday, 14 students
   bought lunch, on Tuesday 12 students bought lunch, on Wednesday 10 students
   bought lunch, on Thursday 15 students bought lunch, and on Friday 12 students
   bought lunch. Which type of graph is the most appropriate to display the data?

   A line graph   C circle graph

   B histogram   D double line graph

Writing Math Which three questions do you ask yourself when
you need to choose an appropriate graph? Explain how their answers
help you to decide which graph to choose.

_____

_____

_____

_____

Hands On: Plot Points on a Coordinate Grid

Problem of the Day ———————————————————— SDAP 1.2

Franklin made a list of the ages of the children at a park. Which age group had the most children? Hint: use 3 equal intervals.
1, 3, 2, 4, 1, 3, 3, 2, 1, 2, 5, 4, 6

Number Sense ———————————————————— KEY

Write the opposite and the absolute value of each integer.

1. 11

2. −7

3. −5

4. 14

Word of the Day ———————————————————— MR 2.0

order

What are some examples of things that go in order?

_____

_____

_____

Facts Practice ———————————————————— KEY

Subtract.

1. 123 − 4.5   **2.** 4.38 − 2.17   **3.** 81.5 − 34.5

4. 9.24 − 5.93   **5.** 18.9 − 7.3

Name _____   Date _____

Hands On: Plot points on a Coordinate Grid

CA Standards
KEY SDAP 1.4, **KEY** SDAP 1.5

Use the coordinate grid to write the ordered pair for each point.

1. A _____

2. B _____

3. C _____

4. D _____

5. E _____

6. F _____

7. G _____

8. H _____

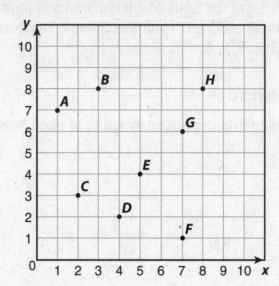

Test Practice

Circle the letter of the correct answer.

9. Heather plotted point M at (3, 4). If Heather wants to draw a straight horizontal line from point M to another point, which ordered pair would fall on the horizontal line?

   A (3, 1)   **C** (6, 4)

   B (3, 2)   **D** (5, 5)

10. Jeremiah plotted point P by starting at the origin, moving right 9 units, and then moving up 8 units. Which ordered pair shows the location of point P?

   A (8, 9)   **C** (9, 9)

   B (9, 8)   **D** (10, 8)

Writing Math If the location of a point is at (6, 0), would the ordered pair lie on the x or y axis? Explain.

_____

_____

_____

_____

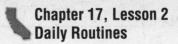

Interpret Graphs of Ordered Pairs

Problem of the Day ─────────────────────── KEY **AF 1.4**

Renee plotted the point (3, 4) on a coordinate grid. She moved to the right four points, and then up three points. Maria says that she plotted the point incorrectly. Which girl is correct?

Algebra and Functions ─────────────────── KEY **AF 1.4**

Use Workmat 7 to locate each point on the coordinate grid.

1. (1, 3)

2. (4, 6)

3. (7, 0)

4. (3, 1)

Number of the Day ───────────────────────── MR 2.0

2

Throughout the day, find examples of things that come in 2s.

_____

_____

_____

Facts Practice ──────────────────────────── NS 1.1

Round each number to the underlined digit.

1. 478,4̲32,567   **2.** 7̲35,298   **3.** 9̲,684,819

4. 389,294̲,984   **5.** 2̲49,587   **6.** 156̲,984

Name _____ Date _____

Interpret Graphs of Ordered Pairs

CA Standards
KEY SDAP 1.4, AF 1.1

The graph shows the number of squares Jane had made for her quilt
by each day over 10 days.

Use the graph of Jane's quilt project to answer problems 1–5 and Writing Math.

1. How many squares had Jane made by
   the second day of her quilt project?

   _____

2. How many squares had Jane made by
   the fifth day?

   _____

3. Jane had made 12 squares by the sixth
   day. When was the next day she worked
   on the project?

   _____

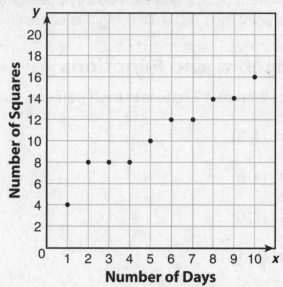

 **Test Practice**

Circle the letter of the correct answer.

4. How many squares had Jane completed
   in one week?

   A 8 squares   **C** 12 squares

   B 10 squares   **D** 14 squares

5. On which three days did Jane not make
   any quilt squares?

   A Day 2, Day 3, and Day 4

   B Day 3, Day 4, and Day 7

   C Day 4, Day 5, and Day 7

   D Day 5, Day 6, and Day 7

Writing Math How do you know how many squares Jane made
in order to complete her quilt project? Explain.

_____

_____

_____

Name _____ Date _____

Graphs of Functions

Problem of the Day

Brad connected the points (2, 5), (2, 8), (4, 8), and (4, 5) on a piece of graph paper. What shape did he make?

Algebra and Functions

In football, a field goal is worth 3 points. Complete the table.

	Field Goals	Points
1.	3	
2.		15
3.	8	
4.		36

Number of the Day

4

The prefix "quad" means four. Make a list of words that contain the prefix quad.

_____

_____

_____

Facts Practice

Solve.

1. $(216 + 52) - 48$

2. $(486 - 28) + 16$

3. $(312 + 19) - 36$

4. $109 + (126 - 35)$

Name _____ Date _____

Graphs of Functions

CA Standards
KEY AF 1.5, KEY SDAP 1.5

Millie bought some fabric for $4 per yard. She had a coupon for $3 off. The total cost of Millie's order can be represented by this function: $y = 4x - 3$, where x is the number of yards of fabric.

Use the information above to answer problems 1–5 and Writing Math.

1. Complete the function table. Find the values for y.

$y = 4x - 3$	
x	y
1	
2	
3	
4	

2. Write the ordered pairs.

3. Use the coordinate grid to plot the points.

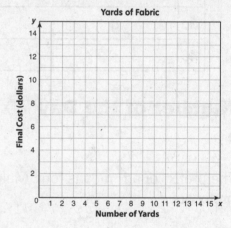

Yards of Fabric

Test Practice

Circle the letter of the correct answer.

4. If Millie bought 6 yards of fabric at $4 a yard, how much money would she have spent?

   A $4.00   c $21.00

   B $12.00   D $24.00

5. Millie bought 3 yards of fabric at $5 a yard and had a coupon for $2 off. How much did she spend?

   A $12.00   c $15.00

   B $13.00   D $16.00

Writing Math How can you use the graph you made in problem 3 to find the amount of money Millie spent if she bought 4 yards of fabric? Explain.

_____

_____

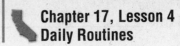
Graphs from Patterns

Problem of the Day ———————————— KEY **AF 1.5**

Mr. Davis orders trophies from the Gold Medal Trophy catalog. The trophies cost $8.00 each and there is a $6 shipping charge per order. Write a function to describe how much money it costs to buy the trophies.

Algebra and Functions ———————————— AF 1.0

Find the value of y when $x = 8$.

1. $15 + x = y$

2. $65 - x = y$

3. $x + 28 = y$

4. $y = 47 + x$

5. $78 - x = y$

Word of the Day ———————————— MR 2.3

square

Name some objects you have seen today that are square.

_____

_____

_____

Facts Practice ———————————— KEY **NS 2.1**

Solve.

1. 36×0.58 **2.** 91×0.08

3. $62 \div 0.2$ **4.** $48 \div 0.16$

Name _____ Date _____

Graphs from Patterns

Ethan made this pattern using blocks.

Figure 1 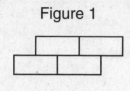   Figure 3 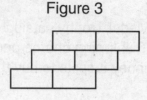   Figure 3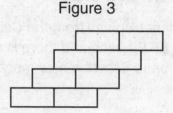

1. Complete the function table.

Figure Number	Number of Blocks
x	*y*
1	
2	
3	

2. Graph the ordered pairs on the coordinate grid.

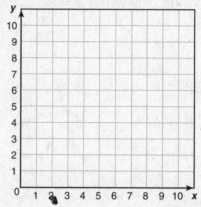

3. Choose the equation for the function.

A $y = 2x$

B $y = 2x + 2$ _____   _____

4. Continue the pattern on the graph to find the number of blocks in Figure 6.

Test Practice

Circle the letter of the correct answer.

5. Ethan used an equation to find the number of blocks in Figure 12. What equation did he use?

A $y = 2(12)$ C $y = 2 + 12$

B $y = (12 \times 2) + 2$ D $y = (12 \times 2) - 2$

6. Ethan continues to add blocks until he reaches Figure 15. Use the equation to find the number of blocks in Figure 15.

A 30 blocks   C 45 blocks

B 32 blocks   D 60 blocks

Writing Math What is another way to find the number of blocks in Figure 15? Explain.

_____

_____

Name _____ Date _____

Problem Solving: Field Trip

Problem of the Day ——————————————— KEY AF 1.5

Rhoda drew the following pattern.

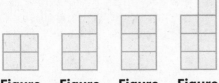

| Figure 1 | Figure 2 | Figure 3 | Figure 4 |

Make a function table.

Figure Number	Number of Squares
x	y

Algebra and Functions ——————————— KEY AF 1.5

Graph the ordered pairs from the function table above. Use values for x from 0–5 and values for y from 0–10. Then, continue this pattern on the graph to find the ordered pair for Figure 5.

Number of the Day ——————————————— KEY AF 1.5

4

Write an equation for the function of a pattern with two variables. Then, use 4 as the value for x and find the value of y. Then, use Learning Tool 40 to graph this ordered pair.

_____

_____

_____

Facts Practice ——————————————————— KEY AF 1.5

Let $x = 3$. Find the value of y.

1. $y = x + 2$ **2.** $y = 4x$

177

Hands On: Measure and Draw Angles

Problem of the Day ———————————————————— MR 1.0

Catherine is stacking cans for a display. She puts 10 cans on the bottom row, 8 cans on the next row, and 6 cans on the next row, and so on until she has one can on top. How many cans will she need to complete the display?

Number Sense ———————————————————— KEY NS 2.3

Identify each as either a "whole number," "fraction or whole number," or "a mixed number."

1. $\frac{12}{3}$

2. 7.345

3. $\frac{13}{5}$

4. $\frac{6}{6}$

Word of the Day ———————————————————— MR 2.3

measure

Make a list of situations when it is useful to measure.

_____

_____

_____

Facts Practice ———————————————————— 4 KEY NS 3.1

Add.

1. $325 + 416 = ?$ 2. $719 + 112 = ?$

3. $409 + 310 = ?$ 4. $192 + 329 = ?$

5. $710 + 315 = ?$

Name _____ Date _____

Hands On: Measure and Draw Angles

CA Standards
KEY MG 2.1, MR 2.2

Look at the four angles. Measure each angle with your protractor and write the measure.

1. ∠AXB _____

2. ∠BXC _____

3. ∠CXD _____

4. ∠DXA _____

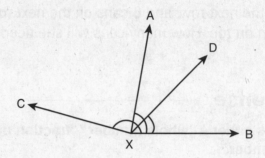

Use a protractor to draw an angle having each measure.

5. 20°   6. 150°   7. 75°   8. 120°

Test Practice

Circle the letter of the correct answer.

9. What is the measure of angle *ABC*?

A 17°
B 45°
C 63°
D 117°

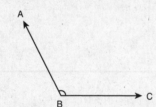

10. What is the measure of angle *MPJ*?

A 40°
B 50°
C 140°
D 150°

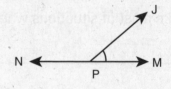

Writing Math When measuring an angle, why do you have to line up one ray of the angle with the zero mark on the protractor?

_____

_____

_____

_____

Name _____ Date _____

Classify Angles

Problem of the Day ———————————————— Prepares for KEY

The sum of the measures of three angles is 180°. One angle measures 40°. Of the two remaining angles, the measure of one is 20° more than the measure of the other. What are the degree measures of the three angles?

Measurement ——————————————————————— KEY MG 2.1

1. Draw an angle of 75°.

2. Draw an angle of 90°.

3. Draw an angle of 110°.

4. Draw an angle of 180°.

Word of the Day ——————————————————————— MR 2.3

angle

Give some examples of the different types of angles you see during the day.

_____

_____

_____

Facts Practice ——————————————————————— 4·KEY NS 3.1

Subtract.

1. 542 − 214 = ?   2. 729 − 202 = ?

3. 809 − 510 = ?   4. 692 − 367 = ?

5. 408 − 156 = ?

Name _____ Date _____

Classify Angles

CA Standard
KEY MG 2.1

Classify each angle as *acute*, *obtuse*, *straight*, or *right*.

1.

2.

3.

4.

_____ _____ _____ _____

Use a protractor to measure each angle. Write the measure.
Classify each angle as acute, obtuse, straight, or right.

5.

6.

7.

8.

_____ _____ _____ _____

Test Practice

Circle the letter of the correct answer.

9. The sum of which two types of angles gives a straight angle?

   A acute angle + acute angle   **C** right angle + right angle

   B acute angle + right angle   **D** obtuse angle + obtuse angle

10. Which angles always form an obtuse angle?

   A 2 acute   **C** 1 right, 1 acute

   B 2 right   **D** 3 acute

Writing Math Suppose you draw a straight line, and then draw a ray from a point on the line at an acute angle to the line. How could you classify the *other* angle that is formed? Explain.

_____

_____

_____

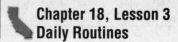
Lines and Line Segments

Problem of the Day —————————————————— KEY MG 2.1

Draw three acute angles so that the sum of the measures is equal to the measure of a right angle.

Number Sense ————————————————— 4 KEY NS 3.0

Find the value of each expression.

1. $180 - (60 + 45)$

2. $180 - 30 - 30$

3. $180 - 62$, then subtract 65

4. 180 minus the sum of 70 and 40

Number of the Day ————————————————— MR 2.3

90

Throughout the day, find examples of numbers that are greater than 90 and less than 90.

_____

_____

_____

Facts Practice ————————————————————— NS 1.0

Solve.

1. 4.5×10^3 **2.** 0.8×10^5

3. $6,700 \div 10^4$ **4.** $900 \div 10^4$

5. 3.2×10^4

Lines and Line Segments

CA Standards
KEY MG 2.1, MR 2.3

Draw each pair of lines.

1. Line $\overleftrightarrow{JM}$ perpendicular to line $\overleftrightarrow{RP}$.

2. Line $\overleftrightarrow{AB}$ parallel to line $\overleftrightarrow{CD}$.

3. Line $\overleftrightarrow{LP}$ and line $\overleftrightarrow{QR}$ intersecting at point X.

Draw each pair of line segments.

4. Line segment $\overline{AJ}$ and line segment $\overline{BG}$ intersecting at point M.

5. Line segment $\overline{HK}$ perpendicular to line segment $\overline{SZ}$.

6. Line segment $\overline{NW}$ parallel to line segment $\overline{QS}$.

Test Practice

Circle the letter of the correct answer.

7. Which of the following best describes the lines in the figure below?

   A parallel

   B intersecting

   C obtuse

   D perpendicular

   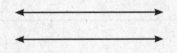

8. Which of the following best describes the line segments in a square?

   A parallel

   B intersecting

   C perpendicular

   D parallel and perpendicular

Writing Math Line $\overleftrightarrow{AB}$ is perpendicular to line $\overleftrightarrow{MN}$. How many right angles are formed where the two lines meet? Explain.

_____

Problem Solving: Field Trip

Problem of the Day

MG 2.3

Dahlia drew the following line art.

Name one pair of lines that is parallel
and one pair that is perpendicular.
Also, name one line segment.

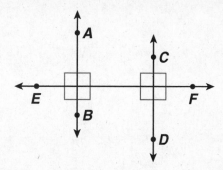

Measurement and Geometry

MG 2.3

1. Draw a pair of lines that is parallel.

2. Draw a pair of lines that is perpendicular.

3. Draw a pair of intersecting line segments that is not perpendicular.

Number of the Day

MG 2.3

90°

What kind of line segments intersect at angles that each
measure 90°?

_____

_____

_____

Facts Practice

MG 2.3

Draw each of the following.

1. point *A*

2. line segment *AB*

3. line *AB*

4. ray *AB*

5. ray *BA*

Name _____ Date _____

Hands On: Sums of Angle Measures

Problem of the Day ———————————————————————— KEY

In Joey's town, First Street and Second Street are always the same
distance from each other. The streets never intersect. What kind of lines
can be used to describe the two streets?

Geometry ———————————————————————————————— KEY MG 2.1

Identify the line pairs as *intersecting, parallel,* or *perpendicular.*

1.

2.

3.

Word of the Day ——————————————————————————— KEY

angle

Find examples of different angles in your classroom. Sketch and label the
angles you find.

_____

_____

_____

Facts Practice ——————————————————————————— KEY

Classify each angle as *acute, right,* or *obtuse.*

1.

2.

3.

4.

Name _____ Date _____

Hands On: Sums of Angle Measures

CA Standards
KEY MG 2.2, **KEY** MG 2.1

**Trace each figure. Use scissors and a straight angle to find
the sum of the measures of the angles for each figure.**

1.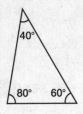
   40°
   80° 60°

   _____

2.

   _____

3.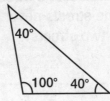
   40°
   100° 40°

   _____

4.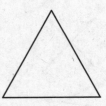

   _____

5.

   _____

6.

   _____

7.

   _____

8.

   _____

Circle the letter of the correct answer.

9. If you divide a pentagon into triangles, what is the least number of triangles you can have?

   A 2   **B** 3   **C** 4   **D** 5

10.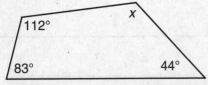
    112°
    x
    83°   44°

    What is the measure of angle *x* in the figure above?

    A 59°   **B** 99°   **C** 121°   **D** 239°

✏️ **Writing Math** How does arranging the torn-out angles of a
triangle on a straight angle help you find the sum of the measures of the
angles?

_____

_____

_____

_____

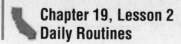
Triangles

Problem of the Day —————————————————— KEY MG 2.2

Maria has a flower garden that is shaped like a triangle. What is the sum of the measures of the angles in the flower garden?

Geometry ——————————————————————————— MG 2.0

Write the name of each figure.

1. ←———→

2. •———•

3. •———→

Number of the Day ——————————————————— KEY MG 2.1

90°

Find examples of objects in your classroom that have 90° angles. Sketch the objects and label the right angle in each.

_____

_____

_____

Facts Practice ———————————————————————— 4 KEY NS 3.1

Find each sum or difference.

1. 177 − 98   2. 180 − 110   3. 56 + 101

4. 89 + 76   5. ⁻45 + 122   6. 180 − 145

Name _____ Date _____

Triangles

Classify each triangle in two ways.

1.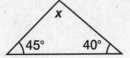

52 yd
48 yd
3 yd

_____

_____

2.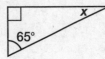

22.627 cm
16 cm
16 cm

_____

_____

3.

8 cm
4 cm   4 cm

_____

_____

4.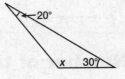

10 m
16 m
18 m

_____

_____

Find the missing angle measures.

5.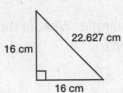

x
45°   40°

_____

6.

65°   x

_____

7.

x
50° 80°

_____

8.

20°
x   30°

_____

Circle the letter of the correct answer.

9. Angel is using a triangular pattern to create a quilt. The sides of the
   pattern measure 8 inches, 6 inches, and 8 inches. What type of triangle
   is Angel's pattern?

   A equilateral triangle   **C** isosceles triangle

   B scalene triangle   **D** obtuse triangle

10.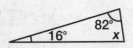

82°
16°   x

   A 8°   **B** 74°   **C** 82°   **D** 98°

Writing Math Is it possible to draw an equilateral
obtuse triangle? Explain your answer.

_____

_____

_____

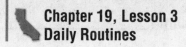
Name _____ Date _____

Quadrilaterals

Problem of the Day ———————————————— MR 2.0

Zia's serving platter is shaped like a triangle. None of the platter's sides are the same length. What kind of triangle is the platter?

Geometry ———————————————————————— KEY MG 2.1

Use a straightedge and a protractor to draw each figure.

1. scalene, right triangle

2. acute, equilateral triangle

3. isosceles, obtuse triangle

Word of the Day ————————————————————— KEY MG 2.1

rectangle

Find as many rectangles in your classroom and on school grounds as you can. Sketch and label the rectangular objects. What do all your rectangles have in common?

_____

_____

_____

Facts Practice ————————————————————— KEY MG 2.2

Two angles in a triangle are given. Find x if x is the third angle in the triangle.

1. 100°, 56°, x **2.** 75°, 88°, x **3.** 135°, x, 16°

4. 25°, 24°, x **5.** x, 112°, 20°   **6.** 65°, x, 75°

Quadrilaterals

CA Standards
KEY MG 2.2, MG 2.0

Classify each figure in as many ways as possible. Then find the missing angle measure.

1.
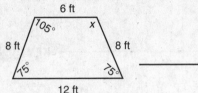

2.
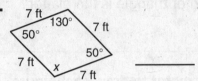

3.
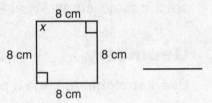

_____   _____   _____

_____   _____   _____

_____   _____   _____

Use this figure to answer Problems 4–5.

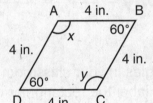

4. What is the measure of *x*? _____

5. What is the measure of *y*? _____

Test Practice

Circle the letter of the correct answer.

6. Eric's class is making kites using quadrilaterals. Each side of Eric's kite is the same length and the opposite sides are parallel. Which figure did Eric use for his kite?

A Rectangle   **C** Parallelogram

B Trapezoid   **D** Rhombus

7. Jane designed an area for a garden in her backyard. She drew a quadrilateral with angles measuring 70°, 41°, and 150°. What is the measure of the fourth angle of the garden?

A 261°   **C** 169°

B 99°   **D** 70°

Writing Math If every square is a rectangle, is every rectangle a square? Explain.

_____

_____

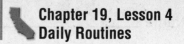
Congruence

Problem of the Day ——————————————— MG 2.0

Mario is fencing in a yard. The yard has 4 sides. The sides are all the same length. What shape could his yard be?

Geometry ——————————————— KEY MG 2.1

Use a straightedge and a protractor to draw each figure.

1. rectangle that is not a square

2. parallelogram that is not a rectangle

3. rhombus that is not a square

Word of the Day ——————————————— MR 2.3

corresponding

Give examples of how *corresponding* is used.

_____

_____

_____

Facts Practice ——————————————— KEY MG 2.2

Three angles in a quadrilateral are given. Find *a*'s measure if it is the fourth angle in the quadrilateral.

1. 115°, 115°, *a*, 65°

2. 129°, 101°, 99°, *a*

3. 135°, *a*, 100°, 25°

4. *a*, 50°, 75°, 205°

Name _____ Date _____

Congruence

Determine if the two figures are congruent. Write *yes* or *no*.

1.
_____

2.
_____

3.
_____

4.
_____

 Test Practice

Circle the letter of the correct answer. Which statement is correct?

5. The two triangles are congruent.

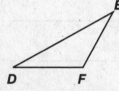 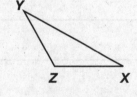

A $\overline{DE} \cong \overline{YZ}$ **C** $\angle F \cong \angle X$

B $\overline{DE} \cong \overline{YX}$ **D** $\angle Z \cong \angle D$

6. $\triangle ABC \cong \triangle DEF$. Find the measure of $\angle F$.

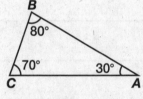 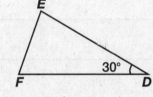

A $30°$ **C** $40°$

B $70°$ **D** $100°$

Writing Math If two triangles are congruent and one is a right triangle, is the other a right triangle? Explain.

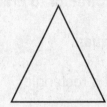 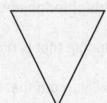

_____

_____

_____

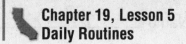
Problem Solving: Missing Angle Problems

Problem of the Day ———————————————— MG 2.0

Daria drew two congruent triangles, $\triangle ABC \cong \triangle DEF$. Which line segment from $\triangle ABC$ is congruent with $\overline{DE}$ from $\triangle DEF$? Explain.

Measurement and Geometry ———————————— MG 2.0

For Exercises 1–3, use the congruent triangles. $\triangle ABC \cong \triangle DEF$

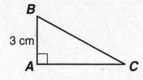 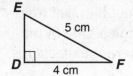

1. Which angle is congruent with $\angle E$?

2. What is the length of $\overline{DE}$?

3. What is the length of $\overline{AC}$?

Number of the Day ————————————————— KEY MG 2.1

90°

Find plane figures around the room that have at least one 90° angle.
Then, decide if these plane figures are congruent.

_____

_____

_____

Facts Practice ———————————————————— Grade 4 MG 3.0

Write each expression in symbols.

1. angle A **2.** line segment LM

3. ray RG **4.** triangle FGH

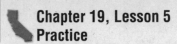
Problem Solving: Missing Angle Problems

CA Standards
MR 2.3, **KEY** MG 2.2

Solve. Explain why your answer makes sense.

1. The floor tiles in Maria's kitchen are shaped like rhombuses.
   One corner of each tile is an angle measuring 50°. What are
   the angle measures of the other three corners?

   _____

2. Howard had a rectangular piece of paper. He cut it in half from
   one corner to another, forming two equal triangles. One of the
   angles of each triangle measured 35°. What were the measures
   of the other two angles?

   _____

 **Test Practice** ━━━━━━━━━━━━━━━━━━━━━━━━━━━

Circle the letter of the correct answer.

3. A walkway is paved with bricks shaped like equilateral triangles. What are the
   angle measures of the bricks?

   A 45°, 45°, 90°   **B** 45°, 45°, 45°   **C** 30°, 60°, 90°   **D** 60°, 60°, 60°

4. The figure is a right triangle. What is the measure of angle x?

   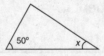

   A 30°   **B** 40°   **C** 50°   **D** 60

Writing Math You have practiced finding missing angle
measures on triangles and quadrilaterals. How could you apply this
skill to figures with more sides?

_____

_____

_____

_____

Hands On: Construct Parallel and Perpendicular Lines

Problem of the Day ———————————————————— MG 2.0

Stephen has 2 display cases that are shaped like congruent rectangles. One display case is 3 ft by 4 ft. What are the dimensions of the other display case?

Geometry ———————————————————————————— MG 2.0

Draw and label each.

1. Line *AB*

2. Angle *XYZ*

3. Line segment *FG*

Word of the Day ————————————————————————— MR 2.3

construct

What does it mean to construct something? Use everyday objects to make constructions. Sketch and describe your constructions.

_____

_____

_____

Facts Practice ——————————————————————————— MG 2.0

Determine if the two figures are congruent. Write *yes* or *no*.

1.

2.

3.

4.

Name _____ Date _____

Hands On: Construct Parallel and Perpendicular Lines

CA Standards
KEY MG 2.1, MG 2.0

Use a compass for Problems 1–3.

1. Draw line *a*. Label a point *B* that is not on *a*. Construct line *k* so that *k* is perpendicular to *a* and passes through *B*.

2. Draw a line and label it *d*. Construct line *e* so that line *e* forms a right angle with *d*. What type of lines are *d* and *e*?

3. Draw a line and label it *c*. Construct line *d* so that line *d* is parallel to *c*.

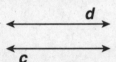

 Test Practice

Circle the letter of the correct answer.

4. Which two points are on parallel lines?

A *Y, A*

B *Y, D*

C *A, D*

D *A, M*

5. Which line is perpendicular to line *m*?

A line *n*

B line *k*

C line *p*

D line *j*

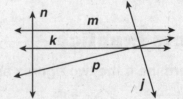

Writing Math Describe the angles that are created where two perpendicular lines intersect.

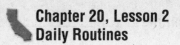
Hands On: Construct Triangles and Rectangles

Problem of the Day ———————————————— KEY MG 2.1

In Den City, Green Street and Red Street are perpendicular to Center Avenue. What kind of lines could be used to represent Green Street and Red Street?

Geometry ———————————————————— MG 2.0

Draw each figure.

1. right triangle *ABC*

2. square *RSTU*

3. rectangle *LMNO*

Word of the Day ———————————————— MR 2.0

congruent

Throughout the day, identify examples of congruency. Describe each example.

_____

_____

_____

Facts Practice ———————————————— KEY MG 2.1

Classify each figure in as many ways as possible.

1.

2.

3.

4.

Name _____ Date _____

Hands On: Construct Triangles and Rectangles

CA Standards
KEY MG 2.1, MR 2.0

Complete the construction.

1. Construct rectangle *CDFG* congruent to rectangle *ABEH*.

A □ B
H □ E

2. Construct triangle *SQM* congruent to equilateral triangle *PNL*.

N △ (P, L)

Test Practice

Circle the letter of the correct answer.

3. Which triangles are congruent?

    A 1, 2

    B 3, 4

    C 4, 2

    D 1, 4

4. Which rectangles are congruent?

    A 4, 1

    B 2, 3

    C 1, 3

    D 2, 4

Writing Math Rich is constructing rectangle *HGJK* congruent to rectangle *SRTQ*. How does knowing that the length $\overline{QT}$ is 4 centimeters help Rich know where to mark point *J*? Explain.

_____

_____

_____

Perimeter and Area of Complex Figures

Problem of the Day ————————————— KEY

Maria constructed the rectangle *DEFG* congruent to rectangle *ABCD*. Side *AB* is parallel to side *CD*. What sides in rectangle *DEFG* are parallel?

Geometry ———————————————— KEY MG 2.1

Use a compass and a straightedge to construct triangle *GHJ* congruent to equilateral triangle *LMN*.

Number of the Day ————————————— KEY NS 2.1

6.8

List different ways to make 6.8. Use addition, subtraction, multiplication, and division.

_____

_____

_____

Facts Practice ———————————————— KEY

Find the sum or product.

1. 23.4×1.5
2. $12.34 + 6.78$
3. $3\frac{1}{4} \times 5\frac{1}{2}$

4. $2\frac{3}{4} + 5\frac{1}{3}$
5. 16.8×4.9
6. $4\frac{2}{5} \times 3\frac{1}{4}$

Name _____ Date _____

Perimeter and Area of Complex Figures

CA Standards
MG 1.0, KEY NS 2.1

Find the perimeter and area of the figure. All corners are right angles.

1.
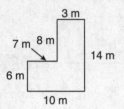

2.
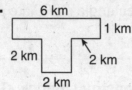

3.
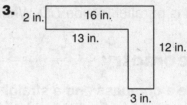

_____   _____   _____

4.
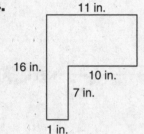

5.
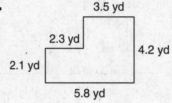

6.
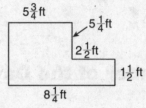

_____   _____   _____

Test Practice

Circle the letter of the correct answer.

7. This is a complex figure. What is the area?

A 40m²

B 53m²

C 109m²

D 130m²

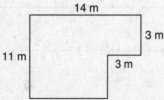

8. This is a complex figure. What is the perimeter

A 124.5 ft

B 102.8 ft

C 426.63 ft

D 768.28 ft

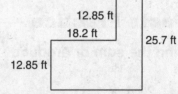

Writing Math Tina is measuring the size of her living room. What is the length of the missing side? Explain how you know.

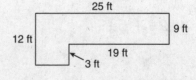

_____

_____

_____

Name _____ Date _____

Problem Solving: Multi-Step Problems

Problem of the Day ———————————————— KEY NS 2.3

Diego drew the outline of his backyard.
What is the area and perimeter of his backyard?

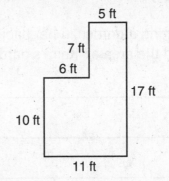

Number Sense Review ———————————————— KEY NS 2.2

Find the perimeter and area of the figure.
All corners are right angles.

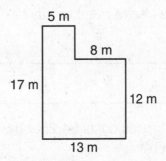

Number of the Day ———————————————— KEY NS 2.2

82

Create a complex figure with at least 6 sides that has a perimeter of 82.

_____

_____

_____

Facts Practice ———————————————— G4 MG 1.0

Find the area and perimeter.

1. rectangle with a length of 3 in. and a width of 5 in.

2. square with sides of 4 cm

3. rectangle with a length of 4 ft and a width of 6 ft

4. square with sides of 5 m

Name _____ Date _____

Chapter 20, Lesson 4
Practice

Problem Solving:
Multistep Problems

CA Standards
MR 1.2, MG 1.0

Solve. Explain why your answer makes sense.

1. Keira is planting a garden in her backyard. Use the
   figure to find the area of Keira's garden.

   _____

   _____

   _____

   [Figure: an L-shaped garden with dimensions: 18 m across the top, 18 m down the right side, 8 m across the bottom, 9 m and 10 m marked in the interior notch]

2. Keira is buying 5-lb bags of topsoil for her garden. Each bag will cover 120 m². How
   many 5-lb bags does Keira need to buy?

   _____

   _____

3. If each 5-lb bag of topsoil costs $4.25, how much will money will Keira spend on the
   topsoil for her garden?

4. Keira plans on putting flower seeds in the rectangular part of her garden that measures
   18 m by 9 m. Each packet of flower seeds will cover 38 m². How many packets of flower
   seeds does Keira need to buy?

   _____

   _____

Test Practice

Circle the letter of the correct answer.

5. The area of a playground is 152 ft². The
   entire area is to be covered in sand. If
   10-lb bags of sand cost $48, and each
   bag covers 16 ft², how much money will
   the sand for the playground cost?

   A $432   C $480

   B $456   D $768

6. A fence is being placed around the
   perimeter of the playground. The
   fence costs $23 for every 6 feet. If the
   fence costs a total of $207, what is the
   perimeter of the playground?

   A 9 ft   C 34.5 ft

   B 10 ft   D 54 ft

Practice
204
Use with text pp. 438–439

Copyright © Houghton Mifflin Company. All rights reserved.

Hands On: Area of Parallelograms

Problem of the Day ———————————————————— MG 1.0

A rectangle has an area of 96 square centimeters and a perimeter of 40 centimeters. What are its dimensions?

Measurement and Geometry ————————————————— MG 1.4

What is the perimeter of a rectangle with a width of 8 inches and a length of 2 feet?

Number of the Day ——————————————————————— MR 2.3

24

Use grid paper to draw some rectangles that have an area of 24 square units.

_____

_____

_____

Facts Practice ————————————————————————— KEY **AF 1.5**

Find the area of each figure.

1.

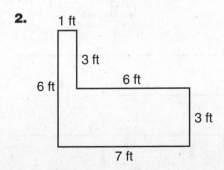

9 m
3 m
5 m
4 m
2 m
5 m

2.

1 ft
3 ft
6 ft
6 ft
3 ft
7 ft

Name _____ Date _____

Hands On: Area of Parallelograms

CA Standards
KEY MG 1.1, MG 1.0

Copy each parallelogram onto centimeter grid paper. Draw a line from a vertex perpendicular to the other side to make a triangle. Cut out each parallelogram. Then cut off the triangular piece. Make the parallelogram into a rectangle. Find the area of the parallelogram.

1. 5 cm
   9 cm

   _____

2. 5 cm
   14 cm

   _____

3. 12 ft
   7 ft

   _____

4. 4 ft
   18 ft

   _____

5. 6 in
   13 in

   _____

6. 11 cm
   10 cm

   _____

Test Practice

Circle the letter of the correct answer.

7. A parallelogram has a base of 6 cm and a height of 9 cm. What is the area of the parallelogram?

   A 15 cm²   C 54 cm²

   B 56 cm²   D 48 cm²

8. Michael and Janine need a carpet for their playroom. The playroom is in the shape of a parallelogram. The base of the parallelogram is 23 feet and its height is 12 feet. What is the area of the playroom?

   A 69 ft²   C 35 ft²

   B 276 ft²   D 266 ft²

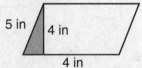

Writing Math Tara said the area of this parallelogram is 20 in². Is she correct? Explain why or why not.

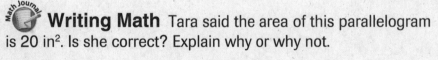

_____

_____

_____

Use with text pp. 452–453

Area of Parallelograms

Problem of the Day ———————————————————— MG 1.0

Mrs. Lambert has a rectangular garden. She used 32 feet of fencing to surround her garden. The length of the garden is 10 feet. What is the area of Mrs. Lambert's garden?

Measurement and Geometry ———————————————— MG 1.0

What is the area of a rectangle with a length of 7 inches and width of 6 inches?

Word of the Day ——————————————————————— MR 2.3

parallelogram

What figures are classified as parallelograms? Why?

_____

_____

_____

Facts Practice ——————————————————— KEY MG 1.1

Find the area of each.

1.
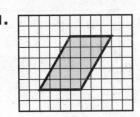

2.

Name _____ Date _____

Area of Parallelograms

CA Standards
KEY MG 1.1, MG 1.0

Find the area of each figure.

1.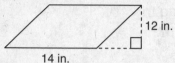

12 in.
14 in.

_____

2.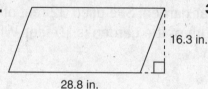

16.3 in.
28.8 in.

_____

3.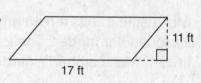

11 ft
17 ft

_____

4.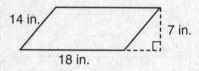

14 in.
7 in.
18 in.

_____

5.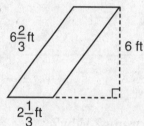

$6\frac{2}{3}$ ft
6 ft
$2\frac{1}{3}$ ft

_____

6.

42 m
30.2 m
23.1 m

_____

Test Practice

Circle the letter of the correct answer.

7. Find the area of a parallelogram that has a base of 14.5 centimeters and a height of 7.2 centimeters.

   A 76.2 cm²   C 98.6 cm²

   B 88.4 cm²   D 104.4 cm²

8. A sandbox is in the shape of a parallelogram. It has a height of 9.6 ft and a base of 8 ft. What is the area of the sandbox?

   A 64.8 ft²   C 76.8 ft²

   B 76.2 ft²   D 76.6 ft²

Writing Math Explain how you found the area of the sandbox in Problem 8.

_____

_____

_____

Hands On: Area of Triangles

Problem of the Day ———————————————————— KEY **MG 1.1**

Evan placed 36 square tiles to make a parallelogram-shaped design.
He used 9 tiles for the base of the design. What was the height of
Evan's design?

Number Sense ———————————————————————— NS 2.4

What is $\frac{1}{2} \times 28$?

Number of the Day ——————————————————————— MR 2.3

48

List the dimensions of parallelograms that would have an area of
48 feet.

_____

_____

_____

Facts Practice ——————————————————————————— MG 1.0

Find the area of each parallelogram.

1. $b = 5$ ft, $h = 7$ ft

2. $b = 12$ in., $h = 9$ in.

3. $b = 20$ cm, $h = 42$ cm

4. $b = 15$ m, $h = 8$ m

Hands On: Area of Triangles

CA Standards
KEY MG 1.1, MG 1.0

Make two copies of each triangle on the same piece of grid paper. Cut out one copy. Place it besides the uncut copy to make a parallelogram. Find the area of the parallelogram. Find the area of the triangle.

1.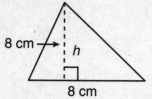

2.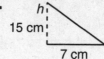

3.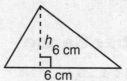

_____ _____ _____

_____ _____ _____

_____ _____ _____

_____ _____ _____

Test Practice

Circle the letter of the correct answer.

4. What would be the area of a scalene triangle with a base measuring 12 cm and a height measuring 7.2 cm?

A 86.4 cm²   C 432 cm²

B 43.2 cm²   D 42.2 cm²

5. Find the area of the triangle.

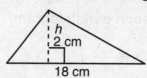

A 18 cm²   C 22 cm²

B 36 cm²   D 72 cm²

Writing Math How does the area of a parallelogram relate to the area of a triangle?

_____

_____

_____

Area of Triangles

Problem of the Day —————————————————————— KEY MG 1.1

A rectangular plot of land has a length of 100 yards and a width of
56 yards. The township has planned to put a playground on half of the
plot of land. What will be the area of the playground?

Measurement and Geometry ————————————————— MG 1.0

What is the base of a parallelogram with an area of 72 square inches
and a height of 4 inches?

Word of the Day ————————————————————————— MR 2.3

triangle

Look around the classroom or in books to find items in the shape of a
triangle. Measure each triangle's base and height.

_____

_____

_____

Facts Practice ————————————————————————— KEY MG 1.1

Find the area.

1.

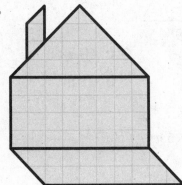

2.

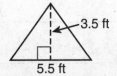
—3.5 ft
5.5 ft

Name _____ Date _____

Area of Triangles

Find the area of each triangle.

1.
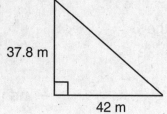
37.8 m
42 m

_____

2.
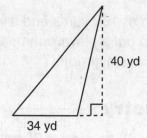
40 yd
34 yd

_____

3.
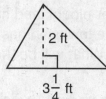
2 ft
$3\frac{1}{4}$ ft

_____

4.
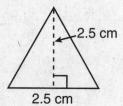
2.5 cm
2.5 cm

_____

5.
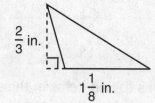
$\frac{2}{3}$ in.
$1\frac{1}{8}$ in.

_____

6.
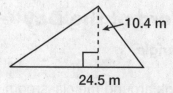
10.4 m
24.5 m

_____

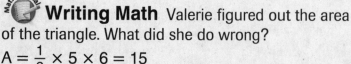

Test Practice

Circle the letter of the correct answer.

7. What would be the area of a scalene
triangle with a base measuring 14 cm
and a height measuring 8.8 cm?

A 61.4 cm²   C 123.2 cm²

B 61.6 cm²   D 22.8 cm²

8. Find the area of the triangle.
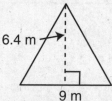
6.4 m
9 m

A 28.8 m²   C 40.5 m²

B 57.6 m²   D 81 m²

Writing Math Valerie figured out the area
of the triangle. What did she do wrong?

$A = \frac{1}{2} \times 5 \times 6 = 15$

$A = 15$ ft²

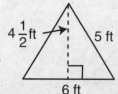
$4\frac{1}{2}$ ft   5 ft
6 ft

Practice
212
Use with text pp. 460–462

Name _____ Date _____

Problem Solving: Field Trip

Problem of the Day ———————————————— MG 1.0

Carlos drew a triangle with a base of 9 inches and a height of 12 inches. Another student said the area of this triangle is 108 sq in. Is the student correct? Explain. If not, give the correct area.

Measurement and Geometry ———————————— MG 1.0

Find the area of each triangle. Draw a diagram if needed.

1. $b = 22$ ft; $h = 11$ ft

2. $b = 23$ m; $h = 11$ m

3. $b = 3\frac{1}{2}$ cm; $h = 2\frac{1}{4}$ cm

Word of the Day ————————————————————— MG 1.0

triangle

Find an object that is the shape of a triangle or has one face that is the shape of a triangle. Use a ruler to measure the base and the height of the triangle and then find its area.

Facts Practice ———————————————————— SDAP 1.1

Find each mode.

1. 8, 8, 7, 7, 6, 8   2. 9, 5, 4, 5, 3, 2

3. 6, 2, 1, 7, 1, 2   4. 9, 4, 3, 5, 7, 8

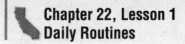
Hands On: Make Solids Using Nets

Problem of the Day ———————————————————— KEY MG 1.1

Brenda is making a flag. How much fabric will she need for the flag if the
base measures 18 inches and the height measures 32 inches?

Number Sense ———————————————————————— KEY NS 2.1

Find the product of 3.2 × 5.1.

Number of the Day ——————————————————————— MG 1.0

18

**Give the dimensions of some triangles and parallelograms that have
an area of 18 square units.**

_____

_____

_____

Facts Practice ———————————————————————— MG 1.0

Find the area.

1. area of a rectangle with length 8.5 ft and width 2.5 ft

2. area of a triangle with base 5.2 yd and height 10 yd

3. area of a parallelogram with base 19 in. and height 20 in.

Hands On: Make Solids Using Nets

CA Standard
KEY MG 1.2

Predict whether the net forms a rectangular prism, a cube, or neither. Then copy the pattern onto grid paper, cut it out, fold it, and tape it together to check your prediction.

1.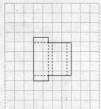
_____

2.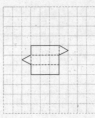
_____

3.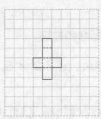
_____

4.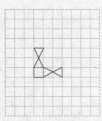
_____

5.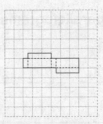
_____

6.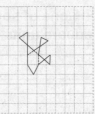
_____

Test Practice

Circle the letter of the correct answer.

7. A net has four rectangles and two squares. It is most likely a net for which solid figure?

A cube

B rectangular prism

C square pyramid

D triangular prism

8. Henry cut out and folded a net that had 6 squares. It is most likely a net for which solid figure?

A cube

B rectangular pyramid

C square pyramid

D triangular prism

Writing Math Lindsay used this net to make a rectangular prism. Is her net correct? Explain why or why not.

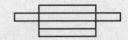

_____

_____

Hands On: Draw Views of Solid Figures

Problem of the Day ———————————————————— KEY MG 1.2

When folded, the figure shown makes a cube. If 3 is on the front face, which number is on the bottom?

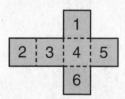

Measurement and Geometry ———————————————— MG 2.0

Name this solid figure. Then, tell how many faces, edges, and vertices it has.

Word of the Day ———————————————————————— MR 2.3

face

Discuss how the word *face* is used in math and in general. Give some examples of when you would use the word *face*.

_____

_____

_____

Facts Practice ———————————————————————— KEY MG 1.2

Tell whether each net form is a rectangular prism, a cube, or neither.

1.

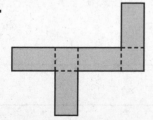

2.

Hands On: Draw Views of Solid Figures

CA Standards
MG 2.3, MG 2.0

Use cubes to build the figure shown. Then draw a top view,
a front view, a right side view, and a left side view
of the figure on grid paper.

1.
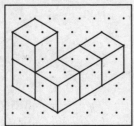

2.
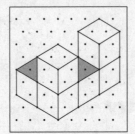

3.
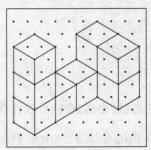

4.
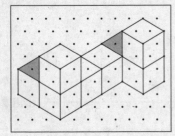

5.
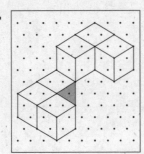

6.

Test Practice

Circle the letter of the correct answer.

7. Justin built the figure out of cubes. How
many cubes did he use?

A 8 cubes
B 7 cubes
C 6 cubes
D 5 cubes

8. Peter built the figure out of cubes. How
many cubes did he use?

A 8 cubes
B 7 cubes
C 6 cubes
D 5 cubes

Writing Math Explain why the figure in Problem 1 has a
different right side view than a left side view.

_____

_____

_____

Name _____   Date _____

Surface Area

Problem of the Day ———————————————— MG 2.3

Draw two-dimensional front, side, and top views for this
three-dimensional figure.

Measurement and Geometry ———————————— MG 2.3

Given these views, draw the figure on dot paper.

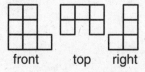

front   top   right

Number of the Day ——————————————————— MR 2.3

6

Throughout the day, find ways to use the number 6.

_____

_____

_____

Facts Practice ——————————————————————— MG 2.0

Identify each figure.

1. 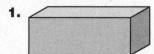   2.   3.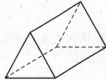

Name _____ Date _____

Surface Area

Predict what solid each net will make. Then find the surface area of the figure. Each square = 1 cm².

1.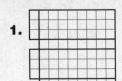

2.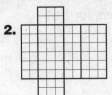

3.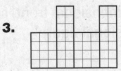

_____   _____   _____

_____   _____   _____

Use the net to determine the surface area of each solid figure.

4.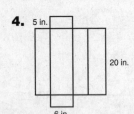
5 in.
20 in.
6 in.

_____

5.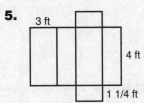
3 ft
4 ft
1 1/4 ft

_____

Test Practice

Circle the letter of the correct answer.

6. Karla is covering a box that is 24 centimeters long, 12 centimeters wide, and 8 centimeters high. How many square centimeters of cloth will she need?

A 576 cm²   C 960 cm²

B 1,152 cm²   D 1,624 cm²

7. Mrs. Steele had just enough wrapping paper to cover a box that measured 15 inches long, 10 inches high, and 6 inches wide. How many square inches of wrapping paper did she have?

A 480 in²   C 600 in²

B 660 in²   D 680 in²

Writing Math What is the difference between a cube and a rectangular prism? Explain.

_____

_____

_____

Volume

Problem of the Day ————————————————— KEY MG 1.2

Colleen has a gift to wrap. The gift is in a box that is 12 inches long,
12 inches wide and 3 inches high. How many square inches of wrapping
paper will she need?

Measurement and Geometry ——————————— MG 1.4

A cube has a surface area of 96 square inches.
What are the dimensions of the cube?

Word of the Day ————————————————————— MG 2.0

cube

Make a list of objects that are cubes.

_____

_____

_____

Facts Practice ————————————————————— KEY MG 1.2

Find the surface area of each figure.

1.

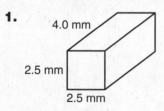

4.0 mm

2.5 mm

2.5 mm

2. a cube in which the length of one edge is 10 inches

Name _____ Date _____

Volume

CA Standard
KEY MG 1.3

Find the volume of each solid figure.

1.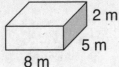
2 m
5 m
8 m

_____

2.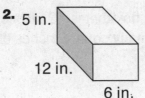
5 in.
12 in.
6 in.

_____

3.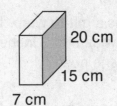
20 cm
15 cm
7 cm

_____

4.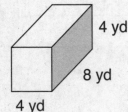
4 yd
8 yd
4 yd

_____

5.
12 in.
12 in.
12 in.

_____

6.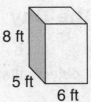
8 ft
5 ft
6 ft

_____

Test Practice

Circle the letter of the correct answer.

7. Leslie built a box that measured 8 inches in length, 4 inches in width, and 7 inches in height. What was the volume of the box?

   A 256 in³

   B 224 in²

   C 224 in³

   D 280 in³

8. Brian's fish tank measured 15 inches in length, 10 inches in width, and 12 inches in height. What was the volume of the tank?

   A 1,980 in³

   B 1,800 in³

   C 1,680 in³

   D 1,620 in³

Writing Math How is finding the volume of a figure different than finding the surface area?

_____

_____

_____

Problem Solving: Perimeter, Area, or Volume?

Problem of the Day

Mario has a box that is 7 ft long, 3 ft wide, and 5 ft high. He wants to use this box to pack cubes that measure 1 ft on each side. How many cubes will fit in the box?

Measurement and Geometry ——————— KEY MG 1.3

Find the volume of each solid figure.

1.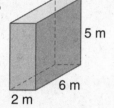
5 m
6 m
2 m

2.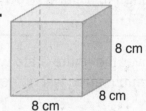
8 cm
8 cm
8 cm

3.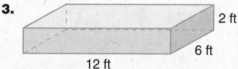
2 ft
6 ft
12 ft

Number of the Day ——————————— KEY MG 1.3

144

Create a rectangular prism that has a volume of 144 units³.

_____

_____

_____

Facts Practice ——————————————— G4 AF 2.0

Solve each equation.

1. $46 \times a = 828$ **2.** $20 \times c = 2{,}160$ **3.** $35 \times v = 665$

4. $3 \times 5 \times r = 270$ **5.** $7 \times 8 \times y = 224$

Perimeter, Area, or Volume?

Solve. Tell whether you found the perimeter, area, or volume.

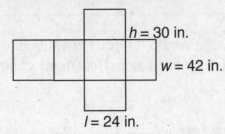

$h = 30$ in.
$w = 42$ in.
$l = 24$ in.

1. Trevor bought his puppy, Sparky, a new dog crate with the net shown above. He needs to find the amount of space inside the crate to make sure it is large enough for Sparky. How much space is inside the crate?

_____

2. Trevor wants to cover the entire crate with fabric at night to keep it dark inside. How much fabric will he need?

_____

3. Trevor is going to place a mat on the floor of the crate. What size mat will he need to cover the entire floor?

_____

Writing Math Explain the difference between finding the area of a face of an object and finding the surface area of an object.

_____

_____

_____

_____

Test Practice

Circle the letter of the correct answer.

4. A fish tank measures 3 feet in length, 2 feet in height, and 2 feet in width. How much water would Joy need to fill the fish tank?

  A 4 ft³   **C** 6 ft³

  B 12 ft²   **D** 12 ft³

5. Eric needs new carpet for his bedroom. His bedroom measures 12 feet by 14 feet. How much carpet does he need?

  A 168 ft³   **C** 168 ft²

  B 160 ft²   **D** 172 ft²

Hands On: Model Percent

Problem of the Day ——————————————————— KEY MG 1.3

A box has a shape of a cube that measures 5 feet on each side.
What is the volume of the box?

Measurement and Geometry ————————————————— MG 1.4

Write the height in inches.

**4 feet
six inches**

Number of the Day ——————————————————— MR 2.3

10

Explain when you might use the number 10 in your day.

_____

_____

_____

Facts Practice ——————————————————————— KEY AF 1.2

Find the product.

1. 21 × 3 = ?   **2.** 50 × 7 = ?   **3.** 140 × 8 = ?

4. 13 × 12 = ?   **5.** 25 × 8 = ?   **6.** 37 × 6 = ?

Daily Routines

225

Use with Chapter 23, Lesson 1

Hands On: Model Percent

CA Standards
KEY NS 1.2, MR 2.3

Write the percent of each grid that is shaded. Then write a decimal and
a fraction in simplest form for the shaded part.

1.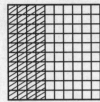

_____

2.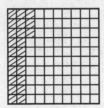

_____

3.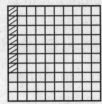

_____

4.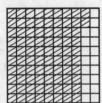

_____

5.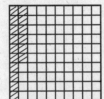

_____

6.

_____

Test Practice

Circle the letter of the correct answer.

7. What is 74% written as a fraction in
   simplest form?

   A $\frac{74}{100}$ C $\frac{37}{50}$

   B $\frac{74}{50}$ D $\frac{37}{10}$

8. What is $\frac{4}{5}$ written as a decimal?

   A 0.2   C 0.45

   B 0.8   D 1.25

 Writing Math Is 7% written as the decimal 0.7 or 0.07?
Explain your answer.

_____

_____

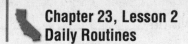
Relate Percents to Fractions and Decimals

Problem of the Day ———————————————————— KEY **NS 1.2**

One-fifth of students have green backpacks. Write $\frac{1}{5}$ as a percent.

Number Sense ————————————————————————— KEY **NS 1.2**

Copy and complete the table.

Decimal	Fraction	Percent
0.80		
	$\frac{7}{50}$	
		30%

Word of the Day ———————————————————————— MR 2.3

centimeter

How can centimeters help you throughout the day?

_____

_____

_____

Facts Practice ——————————————————————— KEY **NS 2.2**

Find each quotient.

1. $12 \div 3 = ?$ **2.** $70 \div 7 = ?$ **3.** $72 \div 6 = ?$

4. $75 \div 5 = ?$ **5.** $90 \div 2 = ?$

Name _____ Date _____

Relate Percents to Fractions and Decimals

CA StandardS
KEY NS 1.2, MR 2.3

Find the percent by finding an equivalent fraction or dividing the numerator by the denominator.

1. $\frac{14}{40}$ _____

2. $\frac{4}{25}$ _____

3. $\frac{1}{4}$ _____

4. $\frac{2}{5}$ _____

5. $\frac{1}{5}$ _____

6. $\frac{12}{25}$ _____

7. $\frac{9}{20}$ _____

8. $\frac{11}{20}$ _____

9. $\frac{3}{5}$ _____

10. $\frac{1}{2}$ _____

11. $\frac{9}{50}$ _____

12. $\frac{13}{25}$ _____

Solve each equation for n.

13. $\frac{50}{100} = \frac{1}{n}$ _____

14. $\frac{75}{100} = \frac{n}{4}$ _____

15. $65\% = \frac{13}{n}$ _____

16. $n\% = \frac{3}{5}$ _____

17. $0.17 = n\%$ _____

18. $0.31 = n\%$ _____

 **Test Practice**

Circle the letter of the correct answer.

19. What is $\frac{3}{10}$ written as a percent.

A 23%

C 30%

B 60%

D 3%

20. What is 0.75 written as a fraction?

A $\frac{75}{50}$

C $\frac{7}{10}$

B $\frac{3}{4}$

D $\frac{1}{7}$

Writing Math Al took a survey and found that $\frac{1}{4}$ of the students in his class favored a field trip to a local lake. What percent of the students favored the trip to the lake? Explain your answer.

Compare and Order Fractions, Decimals, and Percents

Problem of the Day
KEY NS 1.2

Maria and Max played chess after school. Maria won one game out of 2. What percent did Max win?

Number Sense
KEY NS 1.2

Write each fraction as a percent.

1. $\frac{4}{5}$

2. $\frac{1}{10}$

3. $\frac{3}{4}$

4. $\frac{7}{10}$

Word of the Day
MR 2.3

line

How do you use lines during the school day?

_____

_____

_____

Facts Practice
KEY NS 2.1

Find the sum.

1. $0.7 + 0.4 = ?$ 2. $5.4 + 3.2 = ?$ 3. $15 + 0.33 = ?$

4. $7.11 + 2.2 = ?$ 5. $3.4 + 2.9 = ?$

Name _____ Date _____

Compare and Order Fractions, Decimals, and Percents

CA Standards
KEY NS 1.2, MR 2.4

Which is greatest?

1. $\frac{4}{5}$ 0.78 81% _____

2. $\frac{9}{25}$ 0.35 34% _____

3. $\frac{12}{25}$ 5% 0.49 _____

4. $\frac{2}{5}$ 0.41 38% _____

5. $\frac{3}{8}$ 42% 0.38 _____

6. $\frac{13}{20}$ 7% 0.6 _____

7. $\frac{9}{10}$ 0.8 70% _____

8. $\frac{11}{20}$ 50% 0.3 _____

9. $\frac{3}{5}$ 65% 0.64 _____

Which is least?

10. $\frac{8}{25}$ 5% 0.4 _____

11. $\frac{7}{50}$ 20% 0.1 _____

12. $\frac{21}{25}$ 0.8 82% _____

13. $\frac{1}{4}$ 0.3 40% _____

14. $\frac{2}{3}$ 60% 0.06 _____

15. $\frac{7}{10}$ 72% 0.69 _____

16. $\frac{1}{8}$ 12% 0.2 _____

17. $\frac{19}{20}$ 0.9 80% _____

18. $\frac{14}{25}$ 0.5 60% _____

Test Practice

Circle the letter of the correct answer.

19. Which set of numbers is ordered from greatest to least?

    A $\frac{4}{6}$ 0.6 67%   C 23% 0.75 $\frac{8}{9}$

    B 0.83 $\frac{4}{5}$ 71%   D $\frac{2}{5}$ 90% 0.4

20. Order the set of numbers from least to greatest.

    $\frac{7}{25}$ 0.3 20% $\frac{2}{5}$

    A 20% $\frac{7}{25}$ 0.3 $\frac{2}{5}$ C $\frac{7}{25}$ 20% 0.3 $\frac{2}{5}$

    B $\frac{2}{5}$ $\frac{7}{25}$ 20% 0.3   D 0.3 $\frac{2}{5}$ 20% $\frac{7}{25}$

Writing Math Write a number that will make the number sentence true. Explain how you choose the number. $\frac{3}{8} <$ ☐ $< 40\%$

_____

_____

_____

Name _____ Date _____

Percent of a Number

Problem of the Day ———————————————

William finished $\frac{3}{4}$ of a book. Susie finished 72% of the same book. Who read more of the book?

Number Sense ———————————————

Write each decimal as a percent.

1. 0.54

2. 0.44

3. 0.99

4. 0.13

Word of the Day ———————————————

milliliter

During the day, how could you use millimeters?

_____

_____

_____

Facts Practice ———————————————

Find the product.

1. $2 \times 0.12 = ?$ 2. $0.15 \times 4 = ?$ 3. $20 \times 0.1 = ?$

4. $100 \times 0.5 = ?$ 5. $25 \times 0.15 = ?$

Name _____ Date _____

Percent of a Number

CA Standards
KEY NS 1.2, MR 3.2

Solve by writing the percent as a fraction.

1. 35% of 40 = n **2.** 10% of 90 = n **3.** 32% of 25 = n **4.** 44% of 75 = n

_____   _____   _____   _____

5. 56% of 25 = n **6.** 24% of 50 = n **7.** 62% of 150 = n **8.** 75% of 120 = n

_____   _____   _____   _____

Solve by writing the percent as a decimal.

9. 20% of 60 = n **10.** 30% of 70 = n **11.** 83% of 42 = n **12.** 9% of 81 = n

_____   _____   _____   _____

13. 56% of 24 = n **14.** 77% of 35 = n **15.** 42% of 110 = n **16.** 65% of 135 = n

_____   _____   _____   _____

 **Test Practice**

Circle the letter of the correct answer.

17. What is 30% of 80?

   A 3   **C** 24

   B 26   **D** 30

18. What is 55% of 20?

   A 5   **C** 5.5

   B 11   **D** 20

Writing Math Jan says that 10% of 80 is greater than 20% of 40 because 80 is much greater than 40. Is she correct? Explain your answer.

_____

_____

Problem Solving: Percent Problems

Problem of the Day ————————————————— MR 3.2

At lunch, students were able to choose grapes, an orange, or apple slices
to go with their lunches. Fifty students bought lunch and 28% of these
students chose grapes. How many students chose grapes?

Number Sense ————————————————— KEY NS 1.2

Solve by writing the percent as a fraction or decimal.

1. 16% of 75

2. 25% of 50

3. 10% of 30

Number of the Day ————————————————— KEY NS 1.2

20

Find 20% of a number that you have seen throughout your day.

_____

_____

_____

Facts Practice ————————————————— NS 2.0

Multiply.

1. $\frac{1}{2} \times 240$ **2.** $\frac{1}{5} \times 75$ **3.** $\frac{1}{6} \times 3,600$

4. $\frac{1}{3} \times 903$ **5.** $\frac{1}{8} \times 32,000$ **6.** $\frac{1}{4} \times 168$

Problem Solving: Percent Problems

CA Standards
KEY NS 1.2, MR 2.6

Solve. Explain why your answer makes sense.

1. Aaron got a grade of 95% on a test with 60 questions. How many questions did he answer correctly?

_____
_____
_____

2. Janna plays in an orchestra with 40 instruments. Twelve of these are violins. What percent are violins?

_____
_____
_____

3. For Arbor Day, students in Bev's class planted 8 trees. That was 20% of the total number of trees planted by all the students in the school. How many trees did all the students plant?

_____
_____
_____

4. Shirley has 35 photos on the walls in her home. Twenty-one of these are photos of her family. What percent is this?

_____
_____
_____

5. Teresa's class was collecting paper for a recycling drive. They collected 253.5 pounds, which was 84.5% of their goal. What was their goal?

_____
_____
_____

Writing Math Out of the problems above, which problem could you solve using mental math? Explain.

_____

_____

Test Practice

Circle the letter of the correct answer.

6. Out of 475 students at Forrest Elementary School, 285 play on the playground after school at least once a week. What percent is this?

   A 1.6%   C 16%

   B 40%   D 60%

7. If a basketball player makes a basket on 65% of her shots, how many shots has she taken if she gets 52 baskets?

   A 34   C 40

   B 80   D 94

Hands On: Make a Circle Graph

Problem of the Day ———————————————— KEY

Tyler is a waiter at The Steak House. He knows that the restaurant automatically adds an 18% tip to the bill of a large party. If a large group spent $125.00, how much will Tyler receive as a tip?

Number Sense ————————————————————— KEY NS 1.2

Use >, < or = to complete the statement.

1. 0.13 ____ $\frac{3}{20}$

2. 60% ____ $\frac{2}{5}$

3. 18% ____ $\frac{6}{25}$

4. $\frac{7}{16}$ ____ $\frac{1}{2}$

5. 58% ____ $\frac{37}{100}$

Word of the Day ————————————————————— MR 2.3

degree

Name two items that use a degree measurement.

_____

_____

Facts Practice ————————————————————— NS 2.4

Multiply.

1. $\frac{1}{2} \times 52$ 2. $\frac{1}{4} \times 64$ 3. $\frac{2}{3} \times 48$

4. $\frac{3}{5} \times 65$ 5. $\frac{7}{9} \times 72$

Hands On: Make a Circle Graph

CA Standards
KEY NS 1.2, SDAP 1.2

Use the table for Problems 1–4.

1. Multiply each percent by 360°. Write the equations you use.

_____

_____

_____

What Do You Wear?	
Shoe Style	Percent of Students
sneakers	70%
hiking boots	15%
clogs	10%
loafers	5%

2. Draw a circle graph to display the data as percents.

_____

3. If 200 students were surveyed, how many of the students wear sneakers?

_____

4. How many students wear clogs or loafers?

_____

Test Practice

Circle the letter of the correct answer.

5. A survey asked 300 shoppers at the mall where they planned to eat lunch. 45% of them said they would be eating at the mall's food court. How many planned to eat lunch at the food court?

A 45   C 90

B 135   D 150

6. A sticker book contains 30 stickers. If 21 of the stickers are butterflies, what percent of the stickers are butterflies?

A 20%   C 30%

B 60%   D 70%

Writing Math Explain how you found how many students wear clogs or loafers in Problem 4.

_____

_____

_____

Name _____ Date _____

Compare Data Sets

Problem of the Day ——————————————— KEY NS 1.2

Bradley received 48 votes and Susan received 32 votes for student council president. What percentage of votes would a circle graph show that Bradley received?

Number Sense ——————————————— KEY NS 2.3

Simplify.

1. $\frac{25}{40}$

2. $\frac{65}{85}$

3. $\frac{32}{84}$

4. $\frac{5}{60}$

Word of the Day ——————————————— MR 2.3

level

Give an occupation in which a level is used.

_____

_____

_____

Facts Practice ——————————————— KEY NS 1.5

Compare. Use >, <, or = for each.

1. 0.26 ____ 0.62

2. 0.7 ____ 0.65

3. 0.532 ____ 0.53

4. 0.860 ____ 0.86

5. 0.945 ____ 1.02

Name _____ Date _____

Compare Data Sets

CA Standards
SDAP 1.3, KEY NS 1.2

Write each set as a fraction in simplest form and as a percent. Then order the percents from least to greatest.

1. 48 out of 80

_____

2. 36 out of 48

_____

3. 40 out of 160

_____

4. 35 out of 70

_____

_____

Compare. Use >, <, or = ◯ for each.

5. 24 out of 40 ◯ 15 out of 25

6. 10 out of 25 ◯ 14 out of 28

7. 72 out of 90 ◯ 60 out of 80

8. 12 out of 30 ◯ 4 out of 40

 Test Practice

Circle the letter of the correct answer.

9. Mackenzie has 50 novels in her collection. If 30 of them are longer than 100 pages, what percent of her novels are over 100 pages?

A 40%   **B** 60%   **C** 80%   **D** 100%

10. Renata, Bob, and Adam collect seashells. Renata has 46 shells, of which 23 are snail shells. Bob has 40 shells, of which 32 are snail shells. Adam has 12 shells, of which 9 are snail shells. Put the friends in order from least to greatest, according to the percent each has of snail shells.

A Adam, Bob, Renata

C Bob, Adam, Renata

B Adam, Renata, Bob

D Renata, Adam, Bob

Writing Math Annette was comparing 6 out of 20 and 10 out of 15. She said she could tell 10 out of 15 was the greater percent, just by looking at the fractions. How could she tell?

_____

_____

_____

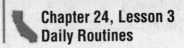
Mental Math: Percent of a Number

Problem of the Day ———————————————— SDAP 1.3

Out of 20 free throws, Kendall makes 16. Out of 15 free-throws Matthew makes 12. Who made the greater percentage of shots?

Statistic, Data Analysis, and Probability ———— SDAP 1.3

Compare. Use >, <, or =.

1. 9 out of 25 ___ 15 out of 30

2. 8 out of 20 ___ 24 out of 60

3. 64 out of 80 ___ 80 out of 100

4. 23 out of 50 ___ 48 out of 100

Number of the Day ————————————————————— MR 2.3

36

Name 3 objects that are 36 inches tall.

_____

_____

_____

Facts Practice ———————————————————————— MR 1.1

Compute mentally.

1. 635×100 2. 218×100 3. $3,500 \div 100$

4. $54,200 \div 100$ 5. $(240 \div 10) \times 10$

Mental Math: Percent of a Number

CA Standards
KEY NS 1.2, NS 1.0

Use mental math to find the number.

1. 75% of 80 _____
2. 20% of 80 _____
3. 50% of 210 _____
4. 10% of 245 _____

5. 25% of 32 _____
6. 10% of 527 _____
7. 50% of 48 _____
8. 75% of 84 _____

 **Test Practice**

Circle the letter of the correct answer.

9. The cost of a winter coat is $150. If the coat is on sale for 20% off, what is the savings?

   A $20

   B $40

   C $30

   D $50

10. The classroom library has 425 books. If 40% of them are novels, how many are novels?

    A 100

    B 150

    C 130

    D 170

Writing Math How can you use mental math to find 40% of a number? Explain using more than one way.

_____

_____

_____

_____

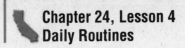
Name _____ Date _____

Problem Solving: Field Trip

Problem of the Day ─────────────────────────── KEY **NS 1.2**

Don found a stereo on sale for 50% off the regular price. The regular price of the stereo is $125. How much will Don save when he buys the stereo on sale?

Number Sense ───────────────────────────────── KEY **NS 1.2**

Use mental math to find the number.

1. 10% of 90

2. 10% of 96

3. 25% of 12

4. 50% of 12

Word of the Day ─────────────────────────────── KEY **NS 1.2**

percent

Look through the newspaper or sale fliers from local stores. Find a sale advertisement giving the percent off the regular price. Share this sale advertisement with the class.

_____

_____

_____

Facts Practice ────────────────────────────────── NS 2.4

Multiply.

1. $\frac{1}{4} \times 24$ 2. $\frac{1}{2} \times 24$ 3. $\frac{1}{3} \times 24$

4. $\frac{2}{5} \times 100$ 5. $\frac{4}{5} \times 100$

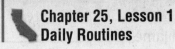
Hands On: Integers

Problem of the Day ——————————————————— KEY NS 1.2

The Samson family had dinner at their favorite restaurant. The total cost of their meal was $60. Use mental math to calculate the tip Mr. Samson left for the waitress if he left 15% of the total bill.

Number Sense ——————————————————— KEY NS 1.2

Solve using mental math.

1. 50% of 160

2. 25% of 120

3. 10% of 90

4. 25% of 400

Word of the Day ——————————————————— MR 2.3

pound

Name 3 items at the grocery store that are weighed in pounds.

_____

_____

_____

Facts Practice ——————————————————— NS 1.1

Round the number 843,709,927 to the place indicated.

1. ten thousands

2. hundred thousands

3. ten millions

4. hundred millions

Hands On: Positive and Negative Numbers

CA Standard
KEY NS 1.5

Write the opposite of each integer.

1. ⁻12

2. ⁻34

3. ⁺9

4. ⁻101

_____

_____

_____

_____

5. ⁻5

6. ⁺212

7. ⁺65

8. ⁻3

_____

_____

_____

_____

Write the absolute value of each integer.

9. ⁻3

10. ⁺11

11. ⁻26

12. ⁻11

_____

_____

_____

_____

Test Practice

Circle the letter of the correct answer.

13. Water freezes at 0° C and boils at ⁺100° C. What other temperature would have the same absolute value as the boiling point, and therefore be the same distance from the freezing point?

   A ⁺200° C   **c** 0° C

   B ⁻100° C   **D** ⁻200° C

14. Which point on the number line has the same absolute value as ⁺3?

   A W   **c** X

   B Y   **D** Z

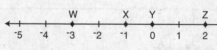

 Writing Math Explain the difference between the opposite of ⁻5 and the absolute value of ⁻5.

_____

_____

_____

_____

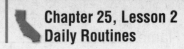
Compare and Order Integers

Problem of the Day ———————————————— KEY NS 1.5

The lowest temperature recorded overnight was 14°F. What is the opposite temperature?

Number Sense ——————————————————— KEY NS 1.5

Write the absolute value of each.

1. 4

2. ⁻21

3. 9.5

4. $\frac{1}{4}$

5. ⁻3.06

Word of the Day ——————————————————— MR 2.3

thermometer

How does a thermometer use positive and negative integers?

_____

_____

_____

Facts Practice ———————————————————— NS 1.0

Find each difference.

1. 175 − 48

2. 462 − 391

3. 1,569 − 402

4. 2,384 − 1,985

5. 1,678 − 1,645

Name _____ Date _____

Compare and Order Integers

CA Standard
KEY NS 1.5

Compare. Draw a number line from ⁻10 to ⁺10 and label each integer.
Write >, <, or = for each ( ).

1. ⁺7 ( ) ⁻6   **2.** ⁻2 ( ) ⁻4   **3.** ⁻4 ( ) 0   **4.** ⁺1 ( ) ⁻1

5. ⁻5 ( ) ⁺10   **6.** 0 ( ) 0   **7.** ⁺6 ( ) ⁻3   **8.** ⁻5 ( ) ⁺1

Write the integers in order from least to greatest. Draw a number line if you wish.

9. ⁻6, ⁻2, ⁻3, 0   **10.** ⁺2, ⁺8, ⁻1, ⁻5   **11.** ⁻7, ⁺2, ⁺1, ⁻1   **12.** ⁻3, ⁺4, ⁻9, ⁻10

_____   _____   _____   _____

_____   _____   _____   _____

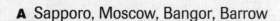

Test Practice

Circle the letter of the correct answer.

13. On the same day in January, the temperature in Bangor, Maine was ⁺14°; in Barrow, Alaska it was ⁻29°; in Sapporo, Japan it was ⁺4°; and in Moscow, Russia it was ⁻14°. Which of the following shows the correct order of cities, from coldest to warmest, on that day?

  A Sapporo, Moscow, Bangor, Barrow

  B Moscow, Barrow, Bangor, Sapporo

  C Bangor, Sapporo, Barrow, Moscow

  D Barrow, Moscow, Sapporo, Bangor

14. Which letter on the number line best identifies the location of ⁻1 ?

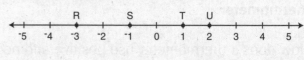

  A R   **C** S

  B T   **D** U

Writing Math How do you know where to place integers on a number line?

_____

_____

_____

Hands On: Add Integers

Problem of the Day ———————————————— KEY NS 1.5

On the same day in January, the temperature in Toledo, Ohio was ⁻2°, in Barrow, Alaska it was ⁻29°, in Moscow, Russia it was 10°, and Chicago, Illinois it was ⁻7°. List the order of the cities from coldest to warmest.

Number Sense ———————————————————— KEY NS 1.5

Order the integers from least to greatest.

1. 3, 7, ⁻1, ⁻6

2. ⁻6, 6, 0, ⁻2

3. ⁻7, ⁻9, 2, 9

4. 12, 5, ⁻2, ⁻8

Number of the Day ————————————————————— MR 2.3

⁻5

Give some examples of when you might see the number 5 or use ⁻5.

_____

_____

_____

Facts Practice ————————————————————————— NS 1.0

Find each sum.

1. 174 + 43   **2.** 462 + 341   **3.** 1,512 + 120

4. 475 + 654   **5.** 145 + 742

Add Integers

CA Standard
KEY NS 2.1

Write the addition expression shown by the counters and then find the sum. White counters are positive. Gray counters are negative.

1. ○○○●●●●●

_____

2. ○○●●●●

_____

3. ○●●●●●

_____

4. ●●●○

_____

5. $^-4 + {}^+3$

_____

6. $^-3 + {}^-3$

_____

7. $^+4 + {}^+1$

_____

8. $^-10 + {}^+2$

_____

Test Practice

Circle the letter of the correct answer.

9. On the first play of the football game, Curtis ran for a 5-yard gain. The next time he carried the ball, he was tackled in the backfield for a 9-yard loss. What was his total yardage on the two plays?

   A $^+14$ C $^+4$

   B $^-4$ D $^-14$

10. At the beginning of one dry season, the level of a certain African river was already 2 feet below normal. It dropped another 5 feet by the end of the season. The next year, the river level began the dry season 3 feet above normal, and dropped another 8 feet by the end of the season. At what time in the 2-year period was the river level the lowest?

    A start of first dry season

    B start of second dry season

    C end of first dry season

    D end of second dry season

Writing Math When you use colored counters to add positive and negative integers, which counters show the sum?

_____

_____

_____

Add Integers on a Number Line

Problem of the Day ———————————————— KEY NS 2.1

During a 3 hole game of golf, a golfer had $+2$ on hole one, -1 on hole two, and -1 on hole three. What is the golfer's overall score?

Number Sense ———————————————————— KEY NS 2.1

Add.

1. $+12 + -6$

2. $-3 + +3$

3. $-5 + +2$

4. $+6 + -2$

5. $+8 + -5$

Number of the Day ————————————————— KEY NS 2.1

8

Write 3 different ways that you can make a sum of 8 using positive and negative integers

_____

_____

_____

Facts Practice ————————————————————— NS 1.0

Add or Subtract.

1. $4,325 - 100$ 2. $679 + 100$ 3. $3,217 + 100$

4. $456 - 100$ 5. $295 + 1,000$

Add Integers on a Number Line

CA Standards
KEY NS 2.1, **KEY** NS 1.5

Use a number line to add.

1. $^+4 + ^-8$

2. $^+7 + ^-10$

3. $^+4 + ^-11$

4. $^-9 + ^+3$

_____

_____

_____

_____

5. $^+8 + ^-6$

6. $^-14 + ^-2$

7. $^-12 + ^+15$

8. $^+7 + ^+5$

_____

_____

_____

_____

Find each sum. Then compare. Write >, <, or =.

9. $^-7 + ^+2$ ◯ $^+1 + ^-6$

10. $^+8 + ^-7$ ◯ $0 + ^-9$

 **Test Practice**

Circle the letter of the correct answer.

11. Which point on the number line could represent $^-3.5$?

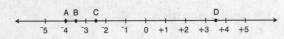

A A

c B

B C

D D

12. Which point on the number line could represent the sum of these four integers: $^-3, ^+7, ^-8, ^+4$?

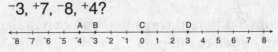

A A

c B

B C

D D

Writing Math When you add one positive number and one negative number, how can you tell whether the sum will be positive or negative?

_____

_____

_____

_____

Use with text pp. 550–552

Problem Solving: Field Trip

Problem of the Day ———————————————— KEY NS 2.1

During the game, Jack first gained 24 points. Then he lost 36 points. Then he gained 18 points. How many points did Jack have in all?

Number Sense ——————————————————— KEY NS 2.1

Use a number line to add.

1. $^-9 + {}^-1$

2. $^-9 + 1$

3. $9 + {}^-1$

Number of the Day ——————————————— KEY NS 2.1

$^-8$

Find a number throughout your day to add to $^-8$. Use a number line to find the sum.

_____

_____

_____

Facts Practice ——————————————————— KEY NS 2.1

Use counters to add.

1. $^-7 + 7$ 2. $18 + {}^-9$ 3. $^-18 + {}^-9$

4. $18 + 9$ 5. $^-18 + 9$

Hands On: Subtract Integers

Problem of the Day ———————————————— KEY NS 2.1

Sunday morning the temperature was ⁻3°F. By the afternoon the
temperature had risen 10°F. What was the temperature in the afternoon?

Number Sense ————————————————————— KEY NS 1.5

Draw a number line from ⁻5 to ⁺5. Label point A at ⁻3 and point B at +2.

Number of the Day ———————————————— KEY NS 1.5

⁻5

List some things that can be represented by the integer ⁻5.

_____

_____

_____

Facts Practice ———————————————————— KEY NS 2.1

Use a number line to find each sum.

1. ⁺4 + ⁻2   **2.** ⁺3 + ⁻7   **3.** ⁺5 + ⁻1

4. ⁻6 + ⁺8   **5.** ⁻3 + ⁺2

Hands On: Subtract Integers

CA Standard
KEY NS 2.1

Use two-color counters to find each difference.

1. $^-4 - {}^+3$ 2. $^+6 - {}^+2$ 3. $^-5 - {}^-1$ 4. $^+4 - {}^-5$

_____   _____   _____   _____

5. $^-5 - {}^-6$ 6. $^+2 - {}^+3$ 7. $^+1 - {}^-9$ 8. $^-2 - {}^+8$

_____   _____   _____   _____

9. $^+7 - {}^+7$ 10. $^+3 - {}^-2$ 11. $^-6 - {}^-9$ 12. $^-4 - {}^+4$

_____   _____   _____   _____

Test Practice

Circle the letter of the correct answer.

13. During a recent dry spell, the water level in a local reservoir dropped 7 feet during July and another 4 feet during August. Which of the following shows how much the water level changed during July and August?

    A $^-7 - {}^-4$ C $^+7 + {}^+4$

    B $^-7 + {}^-4$ D $^-4 - {}^-7$

14. Jake has $5 in his wallet. He owes his sister $8. Which equation represents how much money Jake will have if he pays his sister back?

    A $^+\$5 + {}^+\$8 = {}^+\$13$

    B $^+\$8 - {}^+\$5 = {}^+\$3$

    C $^+\$5 - {}^+\$8 = {}^-\$3$

    D $^+\$5 - {}^-\$8 = {}^+\$13$

Writing Math Which difference is greater, $^+4 - {}^-2$ or $^-4 - {}^+2$? Explain how you found your answer.

_____

_____

Subtract Integers on a Number Line

Problem of the Day ———————————————————— KEY NS 2.1

Gigi and Tony are playing a game. Gigi earned 4 points, then lost 2
points, and then gained 1 point. Tony lost 4 points, gained 5 points, and
then lost 2 points. Who has the greater score? How much greater?

Number Sense ————————————————————————— KEY NS 2.1

Write three addition equations with a sum of ⁻1.

Word of the Day ———————————————————————— MR 2.3

opposite

List some things that are opposite.

_____

_____

_____

Facts Practice ————————————————————————— KEY NS 2.1

Use counters to find each difference.

1. $^+3 - ^-2$ 2. $^-7 - ^-4$ 3. $^+2 - ^+4$

4. $^-5 - ^+1$ 5. $^-2 - ^-6$

Subtract Integers on a Number Line

Use the number line to subtract.

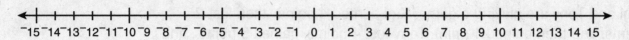

$^{-}15$ $^{-}14$ $^{-}13$ $^{-}12$ $^{-}11$ $^{-}10$ $^{-}9$ $^{-}8$ $^{-}7$ $^{-}6$ $^{-}5$ $^{-}4$ $^{-}3$ $^{-}2$ $^{-}1$ 0 1 2 3 4 5 6 7 8 9 10 11 12 13 14 15

1. $^{+}6 - {^{+}4}$

2. $^{+}7 - {^{-}6}$

3. $^{-}1 - {^{-}6}$

4. $^{+}6 - {^{+}7}$

_____ _____ _____ _____

5. $^{-}5 - {^{+}3}$

6. $^{+}1 - {^{-}8}$

7. $^{+}9 - {^{+}2}$

8. $^{-}2 - {^{+}6}$

_____ _____ _____ _____

9. $^{-}4 - {^{-}2}$

10. $^{+}8 - {^{+}10}$

11. $0 - {^{+}1}$

12. $^{-}8 - {^{-}6}$

_____ _____ _____ _____

Test Practice

Circle the letter of the correct answer.

13. On Monday, the temperature at 7 P.M. dropped 18 degrees below what it had been the day before. On Tuesday, the temperature at 7 P.M. was 14 degrees warmer. What integer shows the overall change in temperature from Sunday to Tuesday?

    A 32 degrees   **C** 12 degrees

    B $^{-}4$ degrees   **D** $^{-}18$ degrees

14. The highest average temperature in Beijing, China is a very hot $^{+}30°C$. The lowest average temperature is 38°C colder than that. What is the lowest average temperature for Beijing?

    A $^{-}8°C$ **C** 0°C

    B 8°C   **D** 68°C

Writing Math Explain how subtraction of integers is related to addition of integers.

_____

_____

_____

Name _____ Date _____

Add and Subtract Integers

Problem of the Day ———————————————————— KEY

I am an integer on a number line. If you start on $^+2$, add $^-3$, and then subtract $^-4$ you will land on me. What integer am I?

Number Sense ———————————————————————— KEY

Write a subtraction sentence in which a positive integer is subtracted from a negative integer and the difference is $^-5$.

Number of the Day ——————————————————————— KEY (NS 1.5)

0

Explain the relationship between 0 and positive and negative integers.

_____

_____

_____

Facts Practice ————————————————————————— KEY (NS 2.1)

Use a number line to find each difference.

1. $^+2 - {}^-4$ 2. $^-7 - {}^-7$ 3. $^+6 - {}^+2$

4. $^-11 - {}^-3$ 5. $^+5 - {}^-5$

Add and Subtract Integers

Predict if the sum or difference is positive or negative. Explain how you decided. Then solve.

1. $^+9 + \,^-8$

_____

_____

_____

2. $^-4 - \,^+9$

_____

_____

_____

3. $^-2 + \,^+4$

_____

_____

_____

_____

Test Practice

Circle the letter of the correct answer.

4. $^+12 - \,^-5 = n$

A $^+17$ C $^-17$

B $^+7$ D $^-7$

5. In which expression does *n* equal a negative integer?

A $^+7 - \,^-9 = n$ C $^+6 - \,^-15 = n$

B $^-3 + \,^+8 = n$ D $^-5 - \,^+11 = n$

Writing Math Susan said that the difference of $^-6 - \,^-7$ will be negative because the two integers have the same sign. Is she correct? Explain why or why not.

_____

_____

Problem Solving: Use a Number Line

Problem of the Day ————————————————— KEY NS 2.1

At 7:00 A.M. Monday morning, the temperature was ⁻4°F.
At 2:00 P.M. Monday afternoon, the temperature was 15°F.
How much had the temperature changed during those 7 hours?

Number Sense ——————————————————————— KEY NS 2.1

Find the sum or difference.

1. ⁺12 + ⁻18

2. ⁺7 − ⁻3

3. ⁻5 − ⁻8

Number of the Day ———————————————————— KEY NS 2.1

⁻4

Find an example during your day when ⁻4 could be used.

_____

_____

_____

Facts Practice ——————————————————————— KEY NS 1.5

Compare. Write >, <, or = in the ⬭.

1. ⁻8 ⬭ ⁺8

2. ⁺7 ⬭ ⁻12

3. ⁻12 ⬭ ⁻8

4. ⁺17 ⬭ ⁺27

5. ⁻2 ⬭ ⁻1

6. ⁻32 ⬭ ⁻40

Name _____ Date _____

Problem Solving: Use a Number Line

CA Standards
KEY NS 1.5, MR 2.3

Use a number line to solve. Explain why your answer makes sense.

1. When Jacob woke up at 7:00 A.M., the temperature was 25°F. By noon, the temperature had risen to 47°F. How many degrees did the temperature change in 5 hours?

_____

2. The high temperature on Monday was 38°F. The high temperature on Tuesday was 4 degrees colder. What was the high temperature on Tuesday?

_____

3. The temperature was reported as 12°F. With the wind chill, the temperature felt as if it were ⁻2°F. What was the difference in temperature due to the wind chill?

_____

4. The ice cream was ⁻5°F when it was first taken out of the freezer. Ryan let it sit at room temperature until it reached 8°F to make it easier to scoop. How many degrees did the temperature increase?

_____

 Writing Math How does a number line help you solve problems with integers?

_____

_____

 Test Practice

Circle the letter of the correct answer.

5. In the beginning of July, the water temperature was 65°F. In the beginning of August, the water temperature was 71°F. How much did the temperature rise during one month?

　A 5°F　　　　**C** 6°F

　B 7°F　　　　**D** 8°F

6. Last February, the temperature measured ⁻6°F on the first day of the month. One week later, the temperature had risen 10°F. What was the temperature one week later?

　A ⁻4°F　　　　**C** ⁻2°F

　B 4°F　　　　**D** 10°F

Hands On: Plot Points in the Coordinate Plane

Problem of the Day ———————————————— KEY NS 2.1

Evan subtracted a negative integer from a positive integer. The difference
was $^+3$. What were the two integers?

Number Sense ——————————————————— KEY NS 2.1

A positive integer is subtracted from a negative integer.
Will the difference be positive or negative? Explain.

Number of the Day ——————————————————— MR 2.3

predict

Explain what it means to predict. Give some examples of things that
people predict.

_____

_____

_____

Facts Practice ——————————————————— KEY NS 2.1

Solve.

1. $^-7 + {}^-1$ 2. $^+2 + {}^-5$ 3. $^-1 + {}^+10$

4. $^-3 - {}^+9$ 5. $^+5 - {}^+2$ 6. $^-4 - {}^-4$

Hands On: Plot Points in the Coordinate Plane

CA Standard
KEY AF 1.4, KEY SDAP 1.5

Use the graph of the figures at the right for Exercises 1–12. Write the ordered pair for each point.

1. G _____   2. A _____

3. M _____   4. I _____

5. J _____   6. N _____

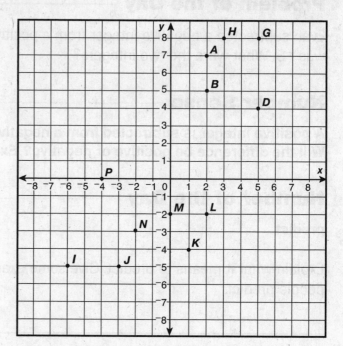

Write the letter name of each point.

7. (⁺2, ⁺5) _____   8. (⁺5, ⁺4) _____

9. (⁺2, ⁻2) _____   10. (⁻4, 0) _____

11. (⁺3, ⁺8) _____   12. (⁺1, ⁻4) _____

Use grid paper. Use the coordinates to plot the given points of figures. Label each point with its letter.

13. A (⁻9, ⁻2)   14. B (⁻4, ⁻5)   15. C (⁻6, ⁺2)   16. D (⁻3, 0)   17. E (0, ⁻3)

18. F (⁺3, 0)   19. G (0, ⁺3)   20. H (⁻5, ⁺3)   21. I (⁻2, ⁻8)   22. J (⁺4, ⁻4)

Test Practice

Circle the letter of the correct answer.

23. In which Quadrant would the ordered pair (⁻7, ⁻8) appear?

A I
B II
C III
D IV

24. Which ordered pair would appear in Quadrant II?

A (⁺5, ⁺7)
B (⁻5, ⁺7)
C (⁻5, ⁻7)
D (⁺5, ⁻7)

Writing Math How can you plot the point (2, 4) on a coordinate plane?

Use with text pp. 586–587

Read a Map

Problem of the Day ——————————————————— KEY SDAP 1.4

Mark plotted five points on a coordinate grid.
Look at his grid. Which point is at (+3, −2)?

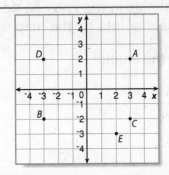

Algebra and Functions ——————————————————— KEY AF 1.4

Plot each point on a coordinate grid.

1. R (−3, −1)

2. S (+4, +2)

3. T (−1, +5)

Number of the Day ——————————————————— KEY SDAP 1.5

−1

Write five ordered pairs that have −1 as one of the coordinates.

_____

_____

_____

Facts Practice ——————————————————— KEY SDAP 1.4

Write the ordered pair for each point.

1. L   **2.** M

3. F   **4.** G

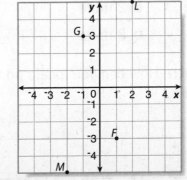

Name _____ Date _____

Read a Map

The location of the animals in the zoo can be found on the coordinate grid map. You can locate points on the map using ordered pairs.

Write the location for the animal.

1. lions _____

2. prairie dogs _____

3. sea turtles _____

4. pandas _____

5. monkeys _____

6. birds _____

Use the map. Write the place that you can see at each location.

7. (⁻4, 3) _____

8. (⁻5, 5) _____

9. (5, ⁻4) _____

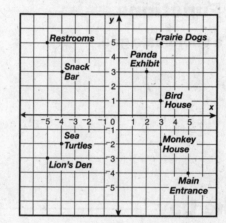

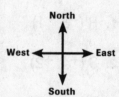

Test Practice

Circle the letter of the correct answer.

10. The map at right shows the location of 4 different reptiles in the Reptile House. Which reptile is at the point (⁻4, 1)?

 A snake   **C** lizard

 B turtle   **D** crocodile

11. How far away are the turtles from the lizards?

 A 4 units   **C** 2 units

 B 6 units   **D** 8 units

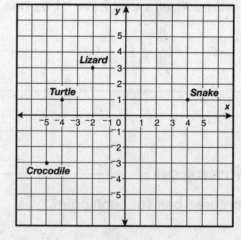

Writing Math How can you locate points on a map using ordered pairs? Explain.

_____

_____

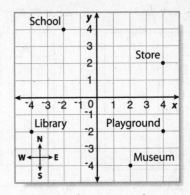
Integers and Functions

Problem of the Day ————————————————— KEY SDAP 1.4

The map shows Rob's neighborhood. His home is at the origin. Rob walked 4 blocks east and 2 blocks south. Where did Rob walk?

Algebra and Functions ———————————— KEY AF 1.4

What ordered pair represents the point that is 5 units north of (+2, ⁻3)?

Word of the Day ———————————————— KEY SDAP 1.5

pair

List some things that come in pairs.

_____

_____

Facts Practice ———————————————— KEY SDAP 1.4

Use the map. Write the point that is at each location.

1. (+3, ⁻2)

2. (+1, +4)

3. (⁻2, +1)

4. (⁻4, ⁻3)

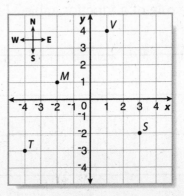

Integers and Functions

CA Standard
AF 1.0, **KEY** AF 1.5

Copy and complete each function table.

1. $y = x + 8$

x	y
-2	
-1	
0	
+1	

2. $y = x - 4$

x	y
+1	
+2	
+3	
+4	

3. $y = 7x$

x	y
0	
6	
9	
12	

4. $y = 5 - x$

x	y
-2	
-1	
0	
+6	

5. $y = 2x + 1$

x	y
0	
1	
3	
4	

6. $y = 2 + x$

x	y
-3	
-2	
-1	
0	

7. $y = 3x - 6$

x	y
0	
+1	
+2	
+3	

8. $y = 4 - x$

x	y
+5	
+7	
+9	
+11	

Test Practice

Circle the letter of the correct answer.

9. The function $k = d - 2$ expresses Kate's age (k) in terms of Don's age (d). How old will Kate be when Don is 51?

A 54 C 48
B 53 D 49

10. Use the function $y = 2x - 15$ to find the value of y when $x = 4$.

A $^-7$ C $^+7$
B $^-5$ D $^+5$

Writing Math How can you use patterns to find the rule of a function table? Explain.

_____
_____
_____
_____

Use with text pp. 590–592

Name _____ Date _____

Graph Functions and Integers

Problem of the Day

KEY SDAP 1.4

Keith plotted the point (⁻5, ⁺2). Louise plotted a point on the same
coordinate grid. Her point was 4 units to the right and 3 units lower than
Keith's point. What were the coordinates of Louise's point?

Statistics, Data Analysis, and Probability

KEY SDAP 1.5

Write an ordered pair for a point that can be found in Quadrant IV.

Word of the Day

MR 2.4

origin

The word origin means beginning or start of something. Choose an item
and research its origin.

_____

_____

_____

Facts Practice

KEY SDAP 1.4

Plot each point on a coordinate grid.

1. (⁻4, ⁺3) point A

2. (⁺3, ⁻1) point B

3. (⁻2, ⁻4) point C

4. (⁺1, ⁺5) point D

Graph Functions and Integers

CA Standard
KEY AF 1.5

**Copy and complete the function table.
Then graph the function in a coordinate plane.**

1. $y = x + 3$

x	y
⁻4	
⁻2	
0	
⁺2	

2. $y = x - 5$

x	y
⁻2	
⁻1	
0	
⁺1	

3. $y = 2x - 1$

x	y
0	
⁺1	
⁺2	
⁺3	

4. $y = 4x + 1$

x	y
0	
⁺2	
⁺4	
⁺6	

5. $y = 7x$

x	y
0	
⁺1	
⁺2	
⁺3	

6. $y = 6 + x$

x	y
⁻3	
⁻2	
⁻1	
0	

7. $y = 2x - 5$

x	y
0	
⁺1	
⁺2	
⁺3	

8. $y = 8 - x$

x	y
⁺1	
⁺2	
⁺4	
⁺6	

Which of these ordered pairs are on the line described by $y = x + 4$?

9. (⁻3, 1)　　　　**10.** (⁻3, ⁻7)　　　　**11.** (2, 6)　　　　**12.** (⁻2, 3)

_____　　_____　　_____　　_____

Writing Math How can you decide if (4, 2) is on the line
described by $y = x - 2$?

_____

_____

Test Practice

13. Which ordered pair is not a solution for
$y = x - 6$?

  A (0, ⁻6)　　　　**C** (1, 7)

  B (10, 4)　　　　**D** (2, ⁻4)

14. Find the ordered pair that is a solution
for $y = 5x + 5$.

  A (4, 20)　　　　**C** (0, 10)

  B (2, 5)　　　　**D** (4, 25)

Problem Solving: Field Trip

Problem of the Day —————————————————— KEY **AF 1.5**

Tanya found sweaters on sale through a catalog. The cost for the
sweaters is $13 each plus $5 shipping per order. Make a function table
to show the total cost for ordering 1, 2, 3, 4, or 5 sweaters.

Algebra and Functions —————————————————— KEY **AF 1.5**

Complete the function table.

Function: $y = {}^-4 - x$

x	y
-2	
0	
2	

Number of the Day —————————————————— KEY **AF 1.5**

$^-9$

Write a function rule as an equation with two variables.
Then, create a function table. Use $^-9$ as one value for x.

_____

_____

_____

Facts Practice —————————————————— KEY **NS 2.1**

Add or subtract. Then, compare. Write <, >, or = for the ⬤.

1. $^-5 + 2$ ⬤ $^-5 - 2$

2. $4 - 3$ ⬤ $^-5 + 6$

3. $^-9 + ^-3$ ⬤ $^-15 + 5$

4. $^-4 + 2$ ⬤ $5 + ^-10$

Hands On: Linear Equations

Problem of the Day ———————————— MR 1.1

Kyle's age is 3 years less than twice Patty's age. Patty is 7 years old.
What equation can you use to find Kyle's age? Solve.

Algebra and Functions ———————————— KEY **AF 1.5**

Solve the function $y = 3x + 1$ when x is $^-2$.

Word of the Day ———————————— MR 2.3

rule

What do you think of when you hear the word rule? Describe some of
the rules you have at home and at school.

_____

_____

_____

Facts Practice ———————————— KEY **AF 1.5**

Complete the function table for $y = 2x - 1$.

	x	y
1.	+3	
2.	+2	
3.	+1	
4.	0	

Name _____ Date _____

Hands On: Linear Equations

CA Standards
KEY SDAP 1.5, KEY AF 1.5

Complete the steps to graph the equation y = x + 3.

1. Make a function table. Use these values for *x*.

x	y
−4	☐
−2	☐
0	☐
+2	☐

2. Write the ordered pairs.

_____

_____

3. Graph the equation.

4. Find two other points on the line and check to see if the coordinates make the equation true.

_____

_____

Test Practice

Circle the letter of the correct answer.

5. Sofia graphed the equation $y = x - 6$. Which ordered pair is NOT on the line for this equation?

   A (0, ⁻6)   **C** (1, 7)

   B (10, 4)   **D** (2, ⁻4)

6. Ray graphed the equation $y = 2x - 5$. Which ordered pair is NOT on the line for this equation?

   A (0, ⁻5)   **C** (3, 1)

   B (5, 2)   **D** (1, ⁻3)

Writing Math How do you find two other points on the line? Explain.

_____

_____

_____

Use with text pp. 604–605

Graphs of Formulas

Problem of the Day ——————————————— KEY AF 1.5

The temperature was 20°F at noon. If the temperature drops 3 degrees each hour, what will the temperature be at 10:00 P.M.?

Algebra and Functions ——————————————— KEY AF 1.5

Write an ordered pair that is on the line described by $y = x - 3$.

Number of the Day ——————————————— KEY SDAP 1.5

0

Count how many times the integer 0 occurs in an ordered pair in the lesson today.

_____

_____

_____

Facts Practice ——————————————— KEY AF 1.4

Identify the quadrant in which each point is located.

1. $(^+1, ^+3)$ 2. $(^+4, ^-1)$ 3. $(^-6, ^+8)$

4. $(^-2, ^-1)$ 5. $(^+5, ^-5)$

Name _____ Date _____

Graphs of Formulas

$A = l \times 6\ m$	
l	A
8 m	48 m^2
9 m	54 m^2
10 m	60 m^2
11 m	66 m^2
12 m	72 m^2

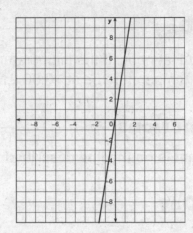

Use the graph above. Find A (area) for each value of l (length). Use the formula to check your answer.

1. $l = 20$ m

2. $l = 6$ cm

3. $l = 11$ ft

_____ _____ _____

Test Practice

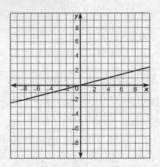

Circle the letter of the correct answer.

4. Which equation could have been used to create the graph above?

   A $4x$ **C** $x - 4$

   B $x + 4$ **D** $x \div 4$

5. Name an ordered pair that could extend the line on the graph above.

   A (5, 20)   **C** (12, 3)

   B (6, 24)   **D** (16, 5)

Writing Math Why can you connect the points on the graph using the area formula? Explain.

_____

_____

Write Equations for Lines

Problem of the Day ———————————————— KEY AF 1.5

If you multiply me by $^-1$, the product is 3. If you add me to 6, the sum is 3. What number am I?

Statistics, Data Analysis, and Probability ———— KEY SDAP 1.5

What ordered pair describes the point that is 3 units to the left and 2 units down from the origin?

Word of the Day ———————————————————— KEY AF 1.5

linear

Linear means in a straight line. Name three things in your classroom, at home, or in the community that are linear.

_____

_____

_____

Facts Practice ———————————————————— KEY AF 1.5

Find one ordered pair for each function.

1. $y = x + 2$ **2.** $y = x - 4$ **3.** $y = 2x$

4. $y = 3x$ **5.** $y = 2x + 3$

Write Equations for Lines

CA Standards
KEY AF 1.5, KEY SDAP 1.4

Write an equation for the graph.

1.
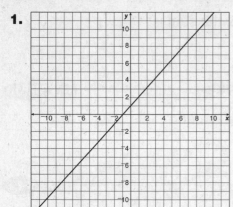

2.
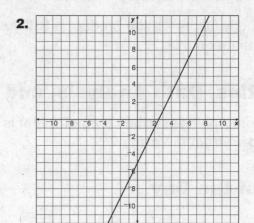

_____

Test Practice

Circle the letter of the correct answer.

3. Which equation could have been used to create this function table?

x	y
⁻1	⁻4
0	⁻3
1	⁻2
2	⁻1

A $y = x + 3$

B $y = 3 - x$

C $y = 2x - 2$

D $y = x - 3$

4. A line is represented by the equation $y = 3x + 2$.

Which ordered pair is located on the line?

A (⁻1, 1)   **B** (4, ⁻2)   **C** (⁻3, ⁻7)   **D** (0, 3)

Writing Math How can you write an equation to show the rule for a function table? Explain.

_____

_____

_____

Equations of Horizontal and Vertical Lines

Problem of the Day ─────────────────────────── KEY AF 1.5

The graph shows the number of inches of rain that fell during a rainstorm. What equation represents this graph?

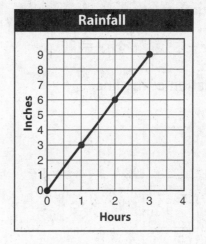

Geometry ─────────────────────────────────── KEY AF 1.4

Graph the coordinates below. Connect the points in the order in which they are listed. Then connect the point in Exercise 4 to the point in Exercise 1. What shape did you make?

1. $(-3, 4)$ **2.** $(3, 4)$

3. $(5, -2)$ **4.** $(-5, -2)$

Words of the Day ──────────────────────────── MR 2.3

horizontal, vertical

Find examples of horizontal and vertical lines in objects around your school during the day. Make sketches and label each example.

_____

_____

_____

Facts Practice ─────────────────────────────── KEY AF 1.5

Graph each equation.

1. $y = x + 3$ **2.** $y = 2x$ **3.** $y = 2x + 2$ **4.** $y = 3x - 1$

Equations of Horizontal and Vertical Lines

CA Standards
KEY AF 1.5, KEY AF 1.4

Graph the equation.

1. $x = {}^-8$ **2.** $y = 1$ **3.** $y = {}^-7$ **4.** $x = 3$

Write the equation of the line.

5.

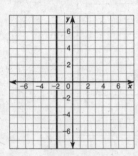

6.

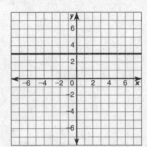

_____   _____

Test Practice

Circle the letter of the correct answer.

7. Line d is represented by the equation $y = 2$.

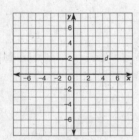

Which ordered pair is located on line d?

A $(0, 2)$

B $(2, 0)$

C $(2, 4)$

D $(0, {}^-2)$

8. Line g is represented by the equation $x = {}^-7$.

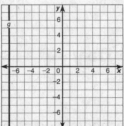

Which ordered pair is located on line g?

A $(1, {}^-7)$

B $(7, 7)$

C $({}^-7, 3)$

D $({}^-2, {}^-7)$

Writing Math How do you know that this function table does not match the equation $y = 8$? Explain.

x	y
1	8
2	7

_____

Name _____ Date _____

Problem Solving: Use a Graph

Problem of the Day ———————————————————— KEY **AF 1.5**

Frances created the following function table for a pattern she created.

x	y
-1	1
0	2
1	3

Greg said the equation that shows the rule of this function table is $y = x - 2$. Is this equation correct? Explain. If not, give the correct equation.

Algebra and Functions ——————————————————— KEY **AF 1.5**

Write an equation to show the rule of the function table.

x	y
-1	-4
0	-3
1	-2

Number of the Day ———————————————————— KEY **AF 1.5**

-5

Write an equation with two variables that involves subtracting 5 or adding -5. Then, create a function table using -1, 0, and 1 for the values of x.

_____

_____

_____

Facts Practice ———————————————————————— KEY **NS 2.1**

Add or subtract.

1. $12 - 19$ **2.** $^-4 - 6$ **3.** $^-8 + 4$

4. $^-7 + 12$ **5.** $^-5 - 2$

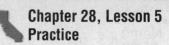
Problem Solving: Use a Graph

CA Standards
MR 2.3, **KEY** SDAP 1.4

The graph and the table show the relationship between the number of pounds of food each astronaut is allowed each day on a space shuttle. One astronaut is allowed 3.8 pounds of food each day.

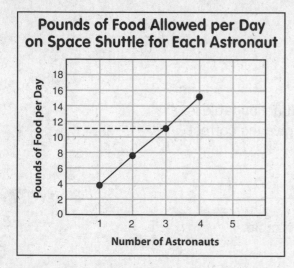

Pounds of Food Allowed per Day on Space Shuttle for Each Astronaut

Number of Astronauts (x)	Pounds of Food per Day (y)
1	3.8
2	7.6
3	11.4
4	15.2

Solve. Use the graph. Explain why your answer makes sense.

1. How many pounds of food per day would be allowed on board for three astronauts?

   _____

2. Write the equation that represents the data in the graph and table.

   _____

 **Writing Math** Explain how to find the number of pounds one astronaut could take aboard if she were going to be in space for 10 days.

_____

_____

Test Practice

Circle the letter of the correct answer.

3. What information is represented on the x-axis on the graph above?

   A number of astronauts

   B pounds of food on board each mission

   C pounds of food per day

   D astronauts' weight in pounds

4. If there were six astronauts on board the shuttle, how many pounds of food would they be allowed each day?

   A 7.6 pounds

   B 11.4 pounds

   C 15.2 pounds

   D 22.8 pounds

Looking Ahead Activities

Next year, you will learn more about
problem-solving with whole numbers
and fractions, geometry, and data.
The Looking Ahead activities will
help you get ready.

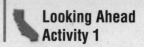
Find the Path

Draw a path through each maze so that each fraction, decimal, or percent on the path is equivalent to the fraction or decimal for that maze. Your path may include horizontal, vertical, or diagonal moves. In each maze, the shaded frames are included to help you find the path.

1. Find fractions, decimals, or percents equivalent to $\frac{4}{5}$.

End

$\frac{5}{6}$	$\frac{8}{12}$	90%	0.02	$\frac{3}{4}$	95%	$\frac{35}{40}$	$\frac{12}{15}$
4.5%	$\frac{1}{5}$	$\frac{9}{15}$	8%	$\frac{1}{5}$	$\frac{60}{75}$	0.80	75%
$\frac{6}{8}$	0.2	80%	$\frac{8}{10}$	0.8	20%	$\frac{8}{12}$	$\frac{10}{15}$
0.45	$\frac{16}{20}$	3/8	54%	$\frac{1}{5}$	0.6	$\frac{3}{4}$	0.08
$\frac{4}{5}$	45%	0.75	$\frac{8}{12}$	15%	$\frac{34}{50}$	0.4	50%

Start

2. Find fractions, decimals, and percents equivalent to 0.6.

End

0.06	6%	$\frac{6}{100}$	$\frac{6}{20}$	16%	$\frac{4}{5}$	$\frac{3}{4}$	0.600
0.006	$\frac{5}{8}$	$\frac{60}{100}$	$\frac{30}{50}$	30%	0.60	$\frac{9}{15}$	$\frac{5}{20}$
$\frac{1}{4}$	60%	0.66	6.0	$\frac{3}{5}$	$\frac{2}{10}$	$\frac{5}{9}$	0.15
$\frac{6}{10}$	0.25	$\frac{3}{10}$	$\frac{2}{5}$	0.606	80%	$\frac{7}{8}$	$\frac{1}{8}$
0.6	0.75	0.12	50%	$\frac{1}{6}$	$\frac{3}{18}$	0.35	$\frac{3}{7}$

Start

Objective: Find equivalent fractions, decimals, and percents.

Decimal Puzzles

CA Standards
KEY NS 2.1 prepares for
Gr. 6 AF 1.2

By yourself

Find the value of each figure. In each puzzle, the same shape will always have the same value.

1.

$1.59	$0.37	◇	◇ = _____
$1.07	$1.59	○	○ = _____
○	◇	△	△ = _____

2.

◇	0.72	4.81	◇ = _____
1.86	○	7.09	○ = _____
△	△	11.90	△ = _____

3.

0.92	1.34	○	2.67	◇ = _____
1.16	3.5	0.86	△	○ = _____
○	◇	1.99	4.53	△ = _____
2.49	6.97	3.26	12.72	

Objective: Add and subtract to solve problems with decimals.

Simplify Fractions

CA Standards
KEY NS 2.3 prepares for
Gr. 6 **KEY** NS 2.4

With your partner

You can simplify fractions using prime factorization.
Find the simplest form of $\frac{12}{18}$.

Step ❶ Find the greatest common factor (GCF) of the numerator and denominator.	**Step ❷** Divide the numerator and denominator by the GCF.

Step ❶ Find the greatest common factor (GCF) of the numerator and denominator.

$12 = \mathbf{2} \times 2 \times \mathbf{3}$

$18 = \mathbf{2} \times \mathbf{3} \times 3$

Multiply the factors that are the same to find the GCF.

The GCF of 12 and 18 is 2×3, or 6.

Step ❷ Divide the numerator and denominator by the GCF.

$\frac{12 \div 6}{18 \div 6} = \frac{2}{3}$

So, $\frac{2}{3}$ is the simplest form of $\frac{12}{18}$.

Write each fraction in its simplest form.

1. $\frac{9}{15}$ 2. $\frac{8}{20}$ 3. $\frac{12}{16}$ 4. $\frac{6}{12}$ 5. $\frac{14}{21}$

_____   _____   _____   _____   _____

6. $\frac{14}{20}$ 7. $\frac{12}{14}$ 8. $\frac{9}{24}$ 9. $\frac{12}{18}$ 10. $\frac{4}{8}$

_____   _____   _____   _____   _____

11. $\frac{8}{12}$ 12. $\frac{20}{24}$ 13. $\frac{6}{8}$ 14. $\frac{12}{24}$ 15. $\frac{6}{15}$

_____   _____   _____   _____   _____

16. $\frac{16}{24}$ 17. $\frac{8}{16}$ 18. $\frac{10}{15}$ 19. $\frac{15}{18}$ 20. $\frac{12}{20}$

_____   _____   _____   _____   _____

Objective: Write fractions in simplest form.

Name _____ Date _____

Fraction Puzzles

Find the value of each figure. In each puzzle, the same shape will always have the same value.

CA Standards
KEY NS 1.2 prepares for Gr. 6 NS 2.1

By yourself

1.

$\frac{1}{2}$	$\frac{3}{8}$	◇	◇ = _____
$\frac{1}{4}$	$\frac{6}{12}$	○	○ = _____
○	◇	△	△ = _____

2.

◇	$\frac{1}{4}$	$\frac{7}{12}$	◇ = _____
$\frac{1}{9}$	○	$\frac{7}{36}$	○ = _____
△	◇	$\frac{7}{9}$	△ = _____

3.

$\frac{1}{24}$	$\frac{1}{24}$	○	△	◇ = _____
$\frac{1}{8}$	$\frac{5}{24}$	△	$\frac{1}{2}$	○ = _____
○	◇	0	$\frac{1}{3}$	△ = _____
◇	$\frac{1}{2}$	◇	1	

Objective: Add and subtract to solve problems with fractions.

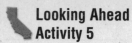

Subtract Integers

CA Standards
KEY NS 2.1 prepares for
Gr. 6 **KEY** NS 2.3

With your partner

Materials: 10 index cards:
1 each numbered 1–10 for
each player

Each row of the table shows a subtraction problem.

Pick one number card. Subtract that number from the given number.

The difference is your score for that turn.

The player with the greatest score wins.

Given Number	Minus	Card Picked	Difference (Score)
8	−		
−4	−		
2	−		
−5	−		
10	−		
−3	−		
3	−		
−6	−		
9	−		
−1	−		
5	−		
−2	−		
		Total Score	

Objective: Subtract positive integers from positive and negative integers.

Name _____ Date _____

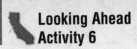
Solving Equations with Addition and Subtraction

CA Standards
KEY AF 1.2 prepares for
Gr. 6 **KEY** AF 1.1

On your own

You can write an equation for the bar model.

$\frac{3}{4}$	
n	$\frac{1}{2}$

You can write an addition equation.

$$\frac{3}{4} = n + \frac{1}{2} \qquad n = \frac{1}{4}$$

You can write a subtraction equation.

$$\frac{3}{4} - n = \frac{1}{2} \qquad n = \frac{1}{4}$$

Write the equation shown by the model. Then solve the equation.

1.
20	
a	14

_____

_____

2.
0.5	
0.35	x

_____

_____

3.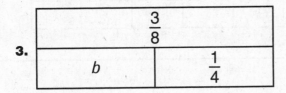
$\frac{3}{8}$	
b	$\frac{1}{4}$

_____

_____

4.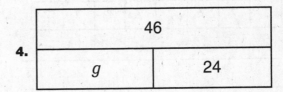
46	
g	24

_____

_____

5.
p	
0.25	0.5

_____

_____

6.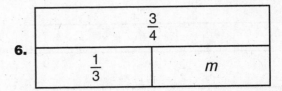
$\frac{3}{4}$	
$\frac{1}{3}$	m

_____

_____

Objective: Use inverse operations to solve addition and subtraction equations.

Name _____   Date _____

Solving Equations with Multiplication and Division

CA Standards
KEY AF 1.2 prepares for
Gr. 6 **KEY** AF 1.1

On your own

You can write an equation for the bar model.

28						
n	n	n	n	n	n	n

Think: What number multiplied by 7 equals 28?

You can write a multiplication equation.

$7n = 28$

$n = 4$

You can write a division equation.

$28 \div n = 7$

$n = 4$

Write the equation shown by the model. Then solve the equation.

1.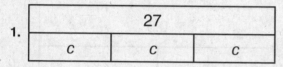

_____

_____

2.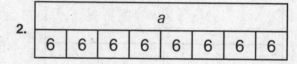

_____

_____

3.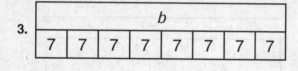

_____

_____

4.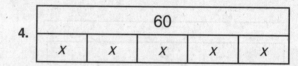

_____

_____

5.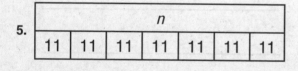

_____

_____

6.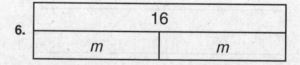

_____

_____

7.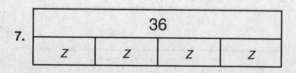

_____

_____

8.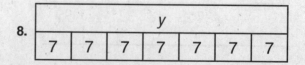

_____

_____

Objective: Use inverse operations to solve multiplication and division equations.

Name _____ Date _____

Proportions

CA Standards
KEY AF 1.2 prepares for Gr. 6
KEY AF 1.1 and **KEY** NS 1.2

On your own

For every 8 blue marbles, there are 3 yellow marbles.
If there are 21 yellow marbles in a bag, how many blue
marbles are in the bag?

Step 1 Write a proportion.

yellow marbles ⟶ $\dfrac{3}{8} = \dfrac{21}{m}$ ⟵ yellow marbles in bag
blue marbles ⟶ ⟵ blue marbles in bag

You know you can show a part to a whole because that is a fraction.

You can show a part to a part as a ratio. $\dfrac{\text{yellow part}}{\text{blue part}}$

Step 2 Use equivalent ratios to solve.

$\dfrac{3}{8} = \dfrac{21}{\square}$

Think: What number multiplied
by 3 equals 21? 7

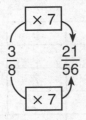

So, there are 56 blue marbles in the bag.

Solve each proportion.

1. $\dfrac{4}{9} = \dfrac{12}{a}$

   $a =$ _____

2. $\dfrac{5}{7} = \dfrac{b}{56}$

   $b =$ _____

3. $\dfrac{2}{c} = \dfrac{28}{42}$

   $c =$ _____

4. $\dfrac{27}{33} = \dfrac{d}{11}$

   $d =$ _____

5. $\dfrac{45}{60} = \dfrac{3}{e}$

   $e =$ _____

6. $\dfrac{20}{f} = \dfrac{10}{9}$

   $f =$ _____

7. $\dfrac{8}{6} = \dfrac{g}{18}$

   $g =$ _____

8. $\dfrac{12}{15} = \dfrac{h}{45}$

   $h =$ _____

9. $\dfrac{4}{24} = \dfrac{i}{6}$

   $i =$ _____

10. $\dfrac{3}{12} = \dfrac{1}{j}$

    $j =$ _____

11. $\dfrac{k}{4} = \dfrac{9}{12}$

    $k =$ _____

12. $\dfrac{7}{l} = \dfrac{28}{32}$

    $l =$ _____

Objective: Solve problems with ratios.

Patterns in Tables of Numbers

CA Standards
KEY AF 1.5 prepares for Gr. 6 AF 2.0

With your partner

Materials: graph paper

For each function table below:

• Find the rule for each table. Write the rule in words and as an equation on the lines below each table.

• Choose numbers from the box to complete the table according to the rule. Numbers in the box are used more than once or they are not used in any table.

• Graph the function on grid paper.

| 3 | 5 | 7 | 8 | 12 | 13 | 15 | 19 | 21 | 27 | 29 | 31 | 36 | 45 | 48 |

1.

x	y
	5
	7
24	8
9	
36	
18	6
27	9

_____

_____

2.

x	y
3	10
14	
19	26
29	36
22	
6	
0	

_____

_____

3.

x	y
9	36
2	
5	20
3	
12	
8	32
	28

_____

_____

4.

x	y
13	
23	18
26	
9	4
20	
34	
16	11

_____

_____

5.

x	y
1	
15	
29	41
27	39
36	
31	43
33	

_____

_____

6.

x	y
9	
7	21
5	
	63
15	
0	0
1	

_____

_____

Objective: Describe the relationship between two sets of related data.

Name _____ Date _____

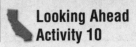
Make a Conversion Table

CA Standards
KEY AF 1.5 prepares for
Gr. 6 AF 2.1

With your partner

Materials: graph paper

You can convert from a temperature in degrees Celsius
to one in degrees Fahrenheit:

• Multiply the Celsius temperature by 9.

• Divide the result by 5.

• Add 32 to the quotient.

For example: 45°C ⟶ 9 × 45 = 405; 405 ÷ 5 = 81; 81 + 32 = 113

So, 45°C is equivalent to 113°F.

1. Write how to convert a temperature in degrees Celsius to one in degrees Fahrenheit
   using words.

   _____

   _____

2. Write the relationships as an equation. Use c to represent degrees Celsius and f to
   represent degrees Fahrenheit.

   _____

3. Use your equation to complete each function table.

°Celsius	0		10		20		30
°Fahrenheit		41		59		77	

°Celsius	0		8		16		24
°Fahrenheit		39.2		53.6		68	

4. Use graph paper to graph the data from each function table.

Objective: Describe the relationship between two sets of related data.

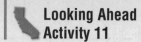
What Did I Measure?

CA Standards
KEY MG 1.3 and MG 1.4 prepare
for Gr. 6 MG 1.3

Begin this activity on your own.

- Measure the dimensions (length, width, and height) of
  2 objects in the classroom (ones that are visible to all students).

- For each object you measure:
  Write the length, width, and height on one sheet of paper.
  Then write a hint about the object you measured
  on the same side of the paper. On the other side,
  write the name of the object.

Now, work with your group.

With a small group

Materials: centimeter ruler
or inch ruler, paper, three-
dimensional classroom
objects

My Guess	What It Really Is

Objective: Measure to find the dimensions of three-dimensional objects.

Name _____ Date _____

What Is the Volume?

CA Standards
KEY MG 1.3 prepares for
Gr. 6 MG 1.3

With your partner
Materials: 60 small cubes

You can build models of
buildings using cubes.

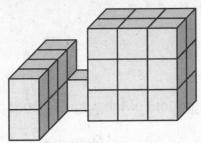

You can estimate the volume and then count
the number of cubes to check your estimate.

You can also use the formula for the volume
of a rectangular prism to find the volume of
each part of a cube model. Then you can
add the parts.

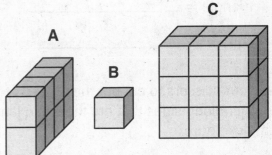

This building is made of 3 rectangular prisms: A, B, and C.
You can find the volume of each prism and add the results.

Volume A = 1 × 2 × 4 = 8 cubic units   Volume B = 1 × 1 × 1 = 1 cubic unit
Volume C = 3 × 2 × 3 = 18 cubic units

Total volume = 8 + 1 + 18 = 27 cubic units

Work with a partner. Follow these steps:

1. Use some of your cubes to make a building. Don't let your partner see how many.

2. Show your building to your partner. Ask your partner to estimate the number of cubes
   you used.

3. Record your partner's estimate. Then break apart your building and show whether that is
   the correct number.

4. Change roles. Now it is your turn to estimate.

5. Make as many buildings as you have time for.

Building	Estimate	Actual Number of Cubes
1		
2		
3		
4		

Objective: Estimate volume in cubic units.

Name _____ Date _____

What is the Area?

CA Standards
KEY MG 1.1 prepares for
Gr. 6 MG 2.0

On your own

Materials: scissors

1. Find the area of each figure at the bottom of the page. Record the area of each.

triangle = _____

rectangle = _____

square = _____

parallelogram = _____

Use your scissors to cut out the figures at the bottom of the page. Put the two figures together along sides that are the same length. Trace the complex figure. Find the area of the complex figure.

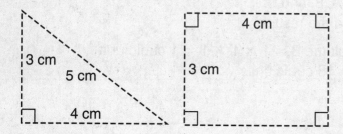

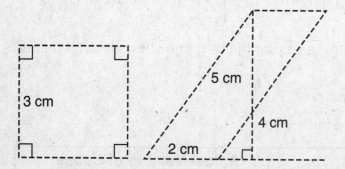

Objective: Find the area of polygons and complex figures.

Name _____ Date _____

Measure Angles

CA Standards
KEY MG 2.1 prepares for
Gr. 6 MG 2.1

On your own

Materials: protractor

Use the street map to solve the problems.

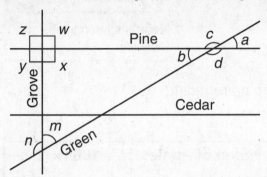

Part 1

Measure the following angles, formed where Pine and Green intersect.

• ∠a _____   • ∠b _____

• ∠c _____   • ∠d _____

• Describe a relationship you see between the angles from Part 1.

_____

_____

Part 2

• What is the measure of ∠m, formed where Grove and Green intersect? _____

• What is the measure of ∠n? _____

• Describe a relationship you see between the angles from Part 2.

_____

_____

Part 3

• What is the measure of all four angles formed where Pine and Grove intersect? _____

• Explain how you know the measures of these angles.

_____

Objective: Measure angles.

Name _____ Date _____

Angle Sums

CA Standards
KEY MG 2.2 prepares for
Gr. 6 **KEY** MG 2.2

On your own

Materials: protractor
(optional)

The sum of the angle measures in a triangle is 180°.
You can use that fact to find the sum of the angle
measures of any polygon.

Complete the table below.
You may check your work by measuring the angles using a protractor.

Figure	Number of Sides	Number of Interior Triangles	Sum of Angles	180° × ?
180°	3	1	180°	180° × 1
180° 180°	4	2	360°	180° × ☐
	5			180° × ☐
				180° × ☐

Objective: Find the sum of angle measures in a polygon.

Name _____ Date _____

Mean, Median, and Mode

CA Standards
SDAP 1.1 prepares for
Gr. 6 SDAP 1.1

On your own

The **mean** is found by dividing the sum of a group of numbers by the number of addends.	The **median** is the middle number when a set of numbers is arranged in order from least to greatest.	The **mode** of the data is the number that occurs most often.

Find the mean, median, and mode for each set of data shown below.
Round the mean to the nearest tenth, if necessary.

1.
Number of Siblings

```
        X
        X
   X    X    X
   X    X    X              X
   X    X    X    X    X    X
 ──────────────────────────────
   0    1    2    3    4    5
```

mean ____ median ____ mode ____

2.
Hours Spent Reading

```
                  X
                  X    X              X
                  X    X    X    X    X
   X    X    X    X    X    X
 ──────────────────────────────
   1    2    3    4    5    6
```

mean ____ median ____ mode ____

3.
Number of Pets

```
   X
   X
   X              X    X              X
   X    X    X    X    X    X
   X    X    X    X    X    X
 ──────────────────────────────
   0    1    2    3    4    5
```

mean ____ median ____ mode ____

4.
Home Runs

```
                  X         X
                  X         X
             X    X         X
        X    X    X    X    X
        X    X    X    X    X    X
 ──────────────────────────────
   0    1    2    3    4    5
```

mean ____ median ____ mode ____

5.
**Age of Students
in Chess Club**

```
                            X
        X         X         X
        X         X    X    X
        X    X    X    X    X
 ──────────────────────────────
   10   11   12   13   14
```

mean ____ median ____ mode ____

6.
Weight of Luggage

```
             X         X
             X         X
        X    X    X    X
        X    X    X    X    X
 ──────────────────────────────
   25   26   27   28   29
```

mean ____ median ____ mode ____

Objective: Identify the mean, median, and mode of a data set.

Name _____ Date _____

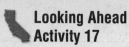
Make a Histogram

Work with your group to take a survey with
results you can record on a histogram.

CA Standards
SDAP 1.2 prepares for
Gr. 6 **KEY** SDAP 2.3

With your group

1. Record your data on the frequency table.

Survey Topic:		
Interval:	Tally	Frequency

2. On your own, make a histogram of the data from your frequency table.

Use your histogram to answer these questions.

3. What is one conclusion you can draw from your histogram?

_____

_____

4. Does your histogram show a positive trend, a negative trend, or no trend? Explain.

_____

_____

Objective: Make and interpret a histogram.

Name _____ Date _____

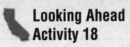
Graphs and Means

For each graph below, find the mean of the data. Draw a horizontal line on the bar graph to show the mean.

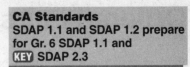

CA Standards
SDAP 1.1 and SDAP 1.2 prepare
for Gr. 6 SDAP 1.1 and
KEY SDAP 2.3

With your partner

The example shows that the mean of the data in the graph is 14 votes.

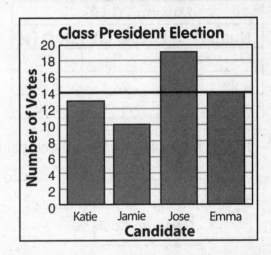

1.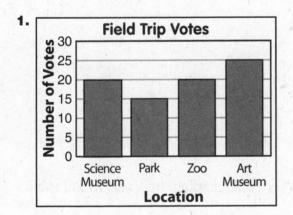

2.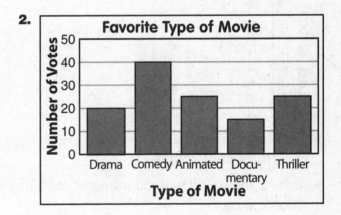

3.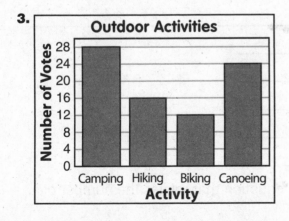

4.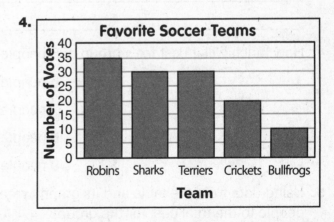

Objective: Display mean for a data set on a bar graph.

Name _____ Date _____

Ordered Pairs

A museum uses the table below to find the cost for
a group to visit the museum.

CA Standards
KEY SDAP 1.4 and **KEY** SDAP 1.5
prepare for Gr. 6 **KEY** SDAP 2.3

On your own

Materials: straightedge

Museum Costs	
Number of People (x)	**Cost (y)**
2	$8
3	$10
4	$12

1. Use the table to write ordered pairs.

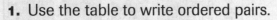

(_____, _____); (_____, _____); (_____, _____)

2. Graph the given coordinates.

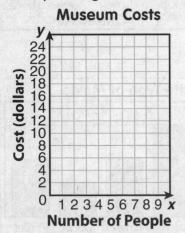

Museum Costs

3. Extend the graph with coordinates for 5 through 9 people. Explain how you found the
coordinates.

_____

_____

4. How much will it cost for a group of 5 people? _____

6 people? _____

7 people? _____

8 people? _____

9 people? _____

5. Using data from the table and its graph, write an equation that relates the number of
people to the total cost for the group.

_____

Objective: Identify and interpret ordered pairs from a graph and write ordered pairs.